Born in 1937, Anton-Andre [...]
attended college at Regensburg, and
studied Political Sciences and Sociology
at Frankfurt/Main. Married, with two
children, he has been editor of
Frankfurter Rundschau since 1967, and
occasionally travels as correspondent to
the Third World.

Ende
A Diary of the Third World War

Anton-Andreas Guha

Translated from the German by Fred Taylor

CORGI BOOKS

ENDE

A CORGI BOOK 0 552 12653 5

First publication in Great Britain

PRINTING HISTORY
Corgi edition published 1986

This book is set in 10/11 pt California

Corgi Books are published by Transworld Publishers Ltd.,
61–63 Uxbridge Road, Ealing, London W5 5SA, in
Australia by Transworld Publishers (Aust.) Pty. Ltd., 26
Harley Crescent, Condell Park, NSW 2200, and in New
Zealand by Transworld Publishers (N.Z.) Ltd., Cnr.
Moselle and Waipareira Avenues, Henderson, Auckland.

Printed in Great Britain by
The Guernsey Press Co. Ltd,
Guernsey, Channel Islands.

Ende
A Diary of the Third World War

26th July

It is war.

The countdown is on. Precise, merciless and inexorable.

A few politicians and generals in Washington and Moscow, creatures of a machine that has become ungovernable, are writing the final chapter of humanity's story, a short story and a grotesque one . . . and we'll be able to say: 'We were there'.

The copy boy had already been shouting it around the corridors: 'Americans attacking Cuban and Soviet installations on Cuba. US airforce in action around the clock. Washington threatens use of tactical nuclear weapons.'

And the information screens in the paper's editorial department flash the latest: 'Soviet strategic nuclear submarines put on alert.'

Even though we have been expecting this development for days – by the hour, in fact – the news overwhelms me. The feeling I have must be like a prisoner's when the judge announces the death sentence: blood drains from my head, I fight against a feeling of helplessness, and my tongue feels like a piece of wood in my mouth. I feel my pulse hammering in my neck, and every beat seems to spell out: OVER – OVER – OVER.

We stare blankly at the glimmering screens, unable to encompass the catastrophe that is developing.

Other people who work for the paper start coming into editorial, white as sheets and unable to say a word. Some are shaking all over. The messenger reads the news out once again.

Then Charlie Lang breaks into the tense silence: 'Well, that's

7

it, friends.' It's the way he usually ends our card games when he's ahead. Now he says it to signal the imminent end of three million years of human evolution, and it doesn't even sound absurd.

Nietzsche's 'pitiless end of that small, over-extended species called Man.'

By every journalistic tradition, we should have been due to bring out an Extra Edition. There were always Extras for disasters and other dramatic world events. The public's excitement gives journalists the feeling of having their finger on the pulse of events, being part of history, being important.

But at the moment all our journalistic instincts are paralysed. After all, what can we tell our readers? We can hardly grasp the seriousness and the real meaning of the news ourselves.

War. Over the years we had got used to describing it as 'inconceivable'. How do you communicate the reality of the inconceivable to your readers?

After about an hour, the shock starts to wear off. The editorial office is almost back to its usual level of chaos. World events – no matter how incredible they may seem – are pushed into the background. Humanity, long sated to the point of boredom by every kind of outrage, has been torn out of its lethargy by a sensation for which none of the usual hackneyed superlatives are adequate. What is about to happen can only be adequately described by the language of the Bible; in the hyperbole of the Apocalypse in which all mankind's myths of the End are gathered together in one terrible vision.

Our total impotence in the face of all this is not simply painful, it strips bare the self-deception that is almost universal in our profession. The press is totally helpless when faced with the developments taking place on the world stage, for those events are determined by an iron, predetermined law of logic. When a hydro-electric dam has burst, of what use are sandbags?

Can we now see that the press has failed in one of its most important tasks – the exposing of structures and social mechanisms, the pillorying of the powerful interests responsible for this situation?

While weapons of the highest technical sophistication were being produced in the laboratories and factories of the

8

superpowers – weapons that defined their own strategic imperatives and demanded a permanent stalemate of hatred and conflict to justify their existence – the press viewed these developments as political phenomena pure and simple, part of that ritualised sequence of summit meetings, ministerial conferences and interviews. As if presidents and chancellors, ministers or even generals were ultimately responsible for deciding on matters of national security.

How was it that the press failed? By not asking the most basic journalistic questions, ones that were as applicable to defence policy as they were in any other area of policy ? Instead, publishers, editors and journalists were happy to justify and approve, though now and again they would pay lip-service to the fact that this 'arms madness' was enough to give us all 'a pain in the gut'.

The conscience of the nation, expressed as stomach pains.

The policy of deterrence has had many justifications. The most idiotic and dangerous argument used in its favour was that everything had worked for decades and that this proved that the balance of terror would hold good for decades more.

I have been driving for twenty-five years now without having an accident. Is this any guarantee that I will not have an accident during the next twenty-five?

The balance of terror is no longer working. Americans and Russians are shooting each other. We used to joke that the next world war would be the last. Now those words sound as hollow as the trumpets of Jericho.

Once the first wave of fear is over, we begin to hope. Everyone starts telling everyone else that the nuclear deterrents of the two superpowers will bring the world to its senses, for there is no other alternative. The American president and the party boss in the Kremlin are both equally aware that there will be no victors in any conflict. This playing with fire is very irresponsible, and it could easily put a match to the fuse of world war, but surely reason will win out? What alternative is there to reason?

We mustn't panic. It's just a matter of keeping our nerve. A cool head is particularly important in a crisis, as our reader article this morning pointed out. Each of us must now do our bit towards a solution. For the rest, we have to trust that the dark clouds on the horizon will clear, for after all, neither the Russians nor the Americans are interested in suicide. There are strong indications that reason is gaining the upper hand in the Kremlin as well as the White House.

Whistling in the dark. Meaningless. A coverup for impotence.

Further news flashes halt the presses running for the national edition of the paper: a naval battle in the Indian Ocean, where both sides have maintained substantial fleets since 1978, keeping each other in check. The reports say that Soviet bombers went into the attack from bases in Afghanistan. The losses on both sides are horrendous. Most of the ships in both fleets have been sunk within the space of two hours.

The agency reports are very unclear. Details are lacking. The course of the naval battle confirms fears that nuclear weapons will be used in the next clash between the superpowers. Neither of them will be drawn into bloody conventional battles, which are unwinnable because of the power of the so-called 'intelligent', pre-programmed weapons. The Russians and the Americans will both try to use tactical nuclear weapons – and to be the first to do so. This strategy is still untried, for no one has yet actually waged nuclear war. The only real test has still to come.

God knows whether the world will still exist when our morning edition appears. The public is getting its information about the fighting from the radio and television news. The station bosses are commenting on the situation in person, their voices heavy with meaning and their faces solemn, as if they had just come from the centres of power.

The indecisive outcome of the naval battle is being made into a virtue; anything to create some hope. The word now is that both sides must realise the futility of any attempt at a military solution. Thus the military clashes have had their positive side. If no one can win by force of arms, there will have to be a way of settling these political disputes at the negotiating table: talks are what we need now.

In fact, we can only grab at straws. We simply have to hope that those responsible in Moscow and Washington will allow themselves to be guided by reason – and that they can halt their war machines even at this stage.

10

There is one simple question that no one is asking: 'They can see reason. *But what if they don't?*' What if Moscow and Washington are equally obsessed with their own survival? What if one side misjudges the other's actions and draws the wrong conclusions? If each side is convinced that the other has clear aggressive intent – on the basis of false assumptions and errors?

It may be that we journalists have realised the importance of this question too late. We should have asked it while there was still time. Deterrence works if both sides operate on the basis of cool, reasoned analysis, if no one makes any mistakes or wrong assumptions, and if each side's estimation of the enemy and his attitude is not distorted by fear. Time and again, in line with general policy, we never really took these things into consideration.

I can see from colleagues' faces that doubts are creeping in, a sense that it may be too late. Too late. And we shall have failed. That will be our fault – the kind of fault that can never be expiated.

The Chancellor comes on at seven. We crowd around the TV set, maybe because we are expecting some kind of salvation: all clear, danger over.

Instead, the Chancellor tells us that he is in constant communication with all allied governments and particularly with the President of the USA. All steps will be considered carefully and amicably before they are agreed on, inasmuch as such steps affect Europe. He is, he says, profoundly convinced that the danger can be averted. This is a testing-time for the Western Alliance: the defence of freedom remains our absolute priority. Only now are we seeing the correctness of the Federal Government's policy of firm adherence to the Western Alliance. Now, when our need is great, we have friends on whom we can rely.

The danger, which he had no desire to understate but which would be averted, must not be allowed to lead to what he called an 'intellectual and moral crisis' in our country. We all had to stick together. The first duty of all citizens was to keep calm. Each of us should stay at his post and do his duty. It was at times of crisis that we Germans always did our duty.

Moreover, the Chancellor said, we had powerful armed forces which would do their duty if necessary, along with those

11

of our allies. The Soviet leadership must realise the risk it was running. He was certain that the Kremlin was in a position to recognise the limits of the situation . . .

The Chancellor did not refer to our risk, which is immeasurably more deadly than that facing the Soviets, and also not to our very limited possibilities, which are about equivalent to those of a fly in a pot of honey.

At the end, the Chancellor made an emotional appeal in the name of the entire German people to the two superpowers to sit down at the conference table. This was now the time to talk.

Depressing. Intellectual and moral inadequacy. Like a refugee, I left the building and walked to the main railway station. Suddenly Frankfurt seemed almost beautiful, a city filled with pulsating life. The evening sun softened the shapes of the bank skyscrapers, those temples of the 20th century. The Kaiserstrasse, the area around the station with its prostitutes and criminals, seemed at that moment to be strangely innocent. The danger that was casting its long shadow over the entire planet made all petty vices and human weaknesses somehow unimportant. The real face of evil was to be found in the seats of government and the military headquarters.

27th July

The editorial department has gone quiet, and there is none of the usual hectic activity. We walk around as if in slow motion, hanging in front of our monitors and reeling like punch-drunk boxers as the latest flashes hit us again and again.

The Americans are dealing with Cuba. Their attempt to move out of their base at Guantanamo was halted by Cuban forces, and this morning they bombed Havana to nothing. The beautiful old city. The smiling, cheeky kids who begged tourists not for money, but for ball-point pens and coloured pencils.

At the same time the US is threatening to land its firefighter forces in Saudi Arabia to crush the pan-Islamic rebels who have deposed the royal house and carried out large-scale massacres. The Soviet Union has been told not to believe that it can avoid responsibility for this serious threat to the West's fundamental interests. The Federal Chancellor is also convinced that the Kremlin is aiming directly at the heart of the Free West and trying to cut off our oil supplies, the lifeline of the West.

In response, the Soviets are mounting a round-the-clock supply operation, flying crack troops and heavy weapons into Ethiopia and North Yemen. Moscow denies having anything at all to do with the coup in Saudi Arabia, and accuses the West of using it as an excuse to launch a last-ditch attack on peaceloving forces. A 'last warning' from TASS to the 'warmongers' in the White House: if the bombing raids on Cuba are not stopped, the Soviet Union will see itself forced to attack a close ally of the USA.

At mid-day, the first demonstrations in the cities. People leave their workplaces and assemble in front of the city halls. Some 50,000 people in front of the Chancellor's office in Bonn. The Römer Square in Frankfurt is filled to overflowing. The crowds make their protests in silence. Hastily-produced placards say: 'We don't want to die', 'Stop this insanity!', 'We only have one world!' and 'What have our children done to you?'

Is the peace movement reviving? If only it isn't too late.

Writers protest against this 'insanity'. Trade unions warn on the need for reason: workers refuse to bear the main burden of suffering yet again. The manipulators and profiteers involved in the arms race must realise that their own necks are on the line now. The trade unions know where their responsibilities lie.

But no call for a general strike.

The committee of the Social-Democratic Party appeals to the Federal Government to make more pressing representations to Washington to avoid a further escalation of the conflict. Also an appeal to Moscow to hold back from threats that lead to escalation.

Everyone's confusion is total. Behind these appeals is nothing more than helplessness, impotence. We are all paralysed, like rabbits faced with a snake.

Sweaty, oppressive summer heat. 35°C. Suffocating.

No clear thoughts or clear line in today's editorial conference. Copy boys were constantly bursting in with more horror stories from the news. An American F-116 fighter-bomber with four nuclear warheads on board has been shot down over Santiago de Cuba. Moscow has emphasised that her strategic nuclear submarines have orders to attack the US base at Guantanamo with atomic weapons if nuclear bombs are dropped on Cuba.

As a result, someone at the editorial conference suggests that we call on our readers and the general public to offer open resistance: the people must now take their fate into their own hands. Deterrence has obviously failed and has therefore lost its only point and purpose, which was to avoid war. If the war were to spread to Europe, the destruction of Germany would be the least of the consequences. We cannot defend ourselves by military means. We have about as much chance of defending our 'democratic basic order' by fighting as the East Germans have of preserving their 'socialist achievements'. The bizarre thing is that we shall be dragged into a war, even though the Soviet Union has no aggressive intentions in Central Europe or against us. The Warsaw Pact has not even mobilised yet. This madness cannot be justified by saying it is in defence of freedom.

The editorial board could not see its way to a decision on this demand. The motion was left on the record for tomorrow. Tomorrow could be too late. Once the war machine is going, no one will be able to stop it. Even mass resistance won't achieve anything then. Nuclear war can be waged without the support of the masses.

The public, if they watch television or listen to the radio, are being deluged with specials and background reports of the most trivial kind, comment, interviews. The Chancellor answers questions, then the Foreign Minister and the Minister of Defence, the General Inspector of the Bundeswehr. Banal questions: 'Do you hold out hope of a negotiated solution to the conflict?'; 'Would you say that our national security policy has proved right despite everything?'; 'Would you say there is any chance of a negotiated settlement?'

Foreign correspondents report on the mood abroad. The British are keeping cool, the French are cautious, and the Americans are relying on their muscle. Wishful thinking. Only the Moscow correspondent has picked up any hint of gloom in the public's mood.

And between these reports, endless commentaries which all come to the conclusion that the Soviet Union has embarked on a high-risk gamble that will have to end sometime. The United States is simply defending freedom – though the Americans too must be prepared to go to the negotiating table.

In this way, listeners and viewers learn from 'reports' that they are simply victims with nothing to do, for others are doing it on their behalf. As if this were some natural disaster that we simply have to wait out in the hope that we don't get caught by it.

When I look at Tina, it seems absurd that we could only have a short time, perhaps a matter of days, to live. Our life together, under normal circumstances, would still have a long way to go to its natural conclusion. But outside events are impinging on our private existences. There is a war going on. If it spreads to Europe, we will both be condemned to death. Along with everyone else.

27th July, midnight

No thought of sleep. Fear and a terrible certainty, then a resurgence of hope: the impossible cannot happen.

Full moon. Taunusrodt is sleeping its way towards dawn. Elsewhere in the town a few windows showing lights. Fear is infectious.

Tina makes us some herb tea 'to calm us'. We are afraid. For our lives, for each other, for Christine and Andreas. When Christine went down to the South of France, she seemed subdued, as if she knew that something was about to happen.

In this she is like my grandmother. I still have a clear memory of the situations in which this usually strong and jolly pleasant woman (she had three long hairs on her chin, which greatly impressed me as a child), would become quiet and turned in on

15

herself. It was then that we would prepare ourselves for some misfortune. My grandfather would grumble and shoo us away from her, because he claimed not to believe in the 'sixth sense'. So far as he was concerned, it was all humbug. But during the meal later he would look at her carefully, trying to read what was in her face. Grandmother's premonitions were usually right. Somewhere in the neighbourhood, there had been a fire, or someone had died unexpectedly.

The nuclear holocaust has been in preparation for so long, has been so long thought about and imagined, that in fact it has come to seem an unavoidable natural phenomenon – like death from old age – and not as a crime against humanity. This war has become possible because both sides have prepared for it, intellectually, morally and materially, with an energy unique in history.

The beginnings of this process are still within easy recall: at the beginning of the Eighties, developments in armaments technology moved with a dramatic swiftness that actually made a successful nuclear 'first strike' a realistic possibility. There was the perfection of submarine location equipment, rapid advances in communications, control and command structures, in laser and particle beam weapons in space, killer satellites with the ability to destroy enemy missiles during flight with a ninety percent chance of success.

In the spring of 1983, the then American President Reagan gave orders for research and development in the area of weapons in outer space. Since the weapons concerned were supposedly 'defensive', the public and the press were successfully misled. Who was going to say anything against 'defence'? 'Defence' is morally justified. Not even the 'evil' Soviets with their powerful missiles could have anything against 'defence'. The trick was that the Americans not only maintained their offensive missiles but actually continued to produce more up-to-date versions in huge quantities.

We say that policies are made by people. This is not true. Policies are carried out by people. Politicians are not the chess players but the pieces on the board. I believe that Nietzsche was right when he saw a 'will to annihilation' at work in human history, an urge towards self-destruction. E.P. Thompson, the

British historian and analyst of the nuclear age, spoke of 'Exterminism'. A kind of determinism.

So long as the USA and the Soviet Union could not attack each other with any hope of success, because both sides had a massive 'second strike' capacity in reserve, even if the first blow were to be devastating, the deterrent effect hinged on the impossibility of waging a successful war. War would have been suicide. When there is a military stalemate and a balance of forces, it is impossible to resolve conflicts through resort to arms, and therefore negotiations are the only way. And so everyone emphasised détente.

From the middle of the 1980s, the possibility of a calculated first strike became real – at first on a theoretical basis in the form of 'limited strategic options', finally as an invitation to a sudden knock-out blow. The thesis of a 'winnable nuclear war' was the end result. For some years the Americans have been preaching that a strategic war can and must be won; for only the victory of the USA in an 'all-out war' will deter the Russians really effectively. And only that degree of deterrence can guarantee world peace.

The USA was the 'guardian of freedom, watching on the walls of the world' – to quote John F. Kennedy, the man who initiated the Vietnam War.

The servility of the 'alliance' relationship here is still impossible to understand. What good to us is any American first-strike capacity? Europe is being used as a hostage. Europe will never be able to defend itself against the USSR.

Stalin was the first to show – despite the fact that he had no nuclear weapons to threaten the USA – that a communist ruling élite will never give way to the threat of force, because it cannot give way without abdicating its power position. And no élite h. s ever abdicated of its own free will. Hitler included. Elites fight on to the bitter end if they are forced to.

Now it looks as if the Soviets will lose the arms race. Western policymakers have been saying for years now that the Kremlin with its nuclear weapons will soon be a paper tiger – a tiger that daren't give in. Just wait a while, you fighters for freedom on the walls of the world, and soon it will be time, and then we'll settle with this nest of vipers, these 'demons of the Twentieth

17

Century' (right-wing German publisher Axel C. Springer on the Russians), these 'rulers of an Empire of Evil' (Reagan).

But it takes two to make war. The Soviet leadership is now looking for a decisive encounter before the Americans can instal fully-developed weapons systems in outer space. The fox is going for the hound's throat. Who is the aggressor?

But developments in armaments technology have dictated not just military strategy, but also politics. This gigantic arsenal has always needed an enemy to legitimise it: deterrence on this scale demanded an 'aggressive' opponent. Total weapons demand a total enemy. Otherwise they would be a criminal monstrosity.

The Soviets could have put on their hair shirt and made a pilgrimage to Washington, and it would have been dismissed as a shabby trick, an attempt to lull the West into relaxing its vigilance. And since they did not do that, but behaved just as was to be expected from an unyielding foe, they confirmed the Americans' image of them as bogeymen. A self-fulfilling prophecy.

The peace movement in the early Eighties was our last chance. Why did it disintegrate? Why was there resignation, disunity, resort to a blinkered policy of action at all costs? Were objective social conditions just too loaded in favour of the existing system? Why didn't the masses join in? Reason was forced to climb down. Reason is always the first to surrender.

I am totally exhausted. Tina has finally fallen asleep.

It is comforting not to be alone at this time.

28th July, mid-day

The American government is absolutely convinced that the Soviets engineered the coup against the Saudi Arabian royal house. The Federal Government in Bonn naturally holds the same view. There is no proof of it. In fact, there is plenty of evidence to the contrary.

Since the middle of the Fifties, there has been a resurgence of Islamic fundamentalism in the Arab countries, a movement of religious renewal with its roots in the Muslim Brotherhoods and

18

the fanatical atmosphere of the seminaries where the Koran is taught.

Its most famous victims: Bhutto in Pakistan, the Shah in Iran, and Sadat in Egypt. The storming of the Grand Mosque in Mecca in 1979. At that time, French troops dressed as Saudis saved the royal house from overthrow.

The arrogant Eurocentric views prevalent in the West could see only oil. There was no understanding of the powerful forces for change working in the Middle East, let alone the causes of these changes. At heart, the Muslim world was defending itself against Western industrial civilisation, which besmirches everything it touches because nothing is sacred except for money, and its only beliefs are in technical progress.

The Saudi-Arabian dynasty was the main promoter of that all-destroying industrial culture which was flooding the Islamic world.

But at the moment, the Soviets are the only people who can be held responsible for this long-predicted coup. They *have* to be responsible so far as the West is concerned. This psychotic system of deterrence creates its own reality, even though it can only function if reason and human understanding are present.

That is the paradox we cannot solve.

More demonstrations today. The public seems to have understood what is happening. Everyone whose position gives them some influence and who can gain the media's attention is appealing for peace. The appeals are flowing thick and fast. But no one is doing anything. Futile posturing. It won't stop the war machine, the process the Americans call 'the doomsday machine'. What a chilling – and suitable – name!

But the fact that the population is becoming distrustful and restless should have an effect on the government in Bonn. We have to tell the Americans: 'Thus far and no further, or we quit. If you want a war, do it without us'.

In the office we consider the difficult question of whether we ought to call on our readers to revolt. In view of our paper's respected position, it would act as a signal to other parts of the media. I know there is a lot of support in other papers too.

Events are overtaking us. There is no sense in producing news that is out of date by the time the paper appears the next morning. Our job now should be to provide some kind of political orientation, a guide to self-help for the average citizen. The people will have to take their own fate into their hands, for the politicians have obviously failed. The politics of 'national security' have become the politics of annihilation, and Europe – certainly both parts of Germany, whatever happens – will fall victim to this chain of events if the war spreads from the Caribbean and the Middle East.

The two superpowers are playing an insane game: the Soviets Russian Roulette, the Americans poker. The Kremlin seems willing to risk a nuclear confrontation – despite the threat to its second-strike capability – while the USA has no intention of being robbed of imminent victory over its arch-rivals.

The Soviet leadership knows what will happen if it cannot stop the Americans from stationing nuclear weapons in space. American strategists have threatened them often enough with 'decapitation'.

Spooky but realistic scenario: the Americans only need to threaten to attack a Soviet city of more than 200,000 inhabitants in order to unleash a panic that could lead to the overthrow of the *Nomenklatura*. This and similar plans have been public knowledge for some time. The war games have been played through over and over again. Strategic nuclear war has been tried and tested out in all its variations. They are ready.

The Soviet political and military élite is massing for the final conflict. It will defend itself with all the means at its disposal – while it still can – even if the price is a worldwide holocaust. For the leadership, the prospect of surrender is more terrifying than the present confrontation with the USA.

The policy of deterrence has lost its deterrent effect for the Soviets. And also for the Americans: they believe they have a chance of forcing the Soviets to their knees.

We have to make this clear to our readers.

When the balance of fear is no longer working, it is time for Europe to abandon this so-called 'security policy'. The obligations of an ally can all too quickly become chains that bind. If the two superpowers choose to run the risk of nuclear confrontation, with all its unpredictable consequences, they can reduce their risk by conducting it in Europe. They can even 'defend' themselves in Europe – to the last West or East German. For them the notion of 'defence' makes sense. All we Germans can do is hit the dirt and hope for the best.

The editor is hesitating. He has reservations, feels torn. An open summons to insurrection could be interpreted as treason, even though the emergency laws are not yet in force. If the two superpowers manage to contain the conflict – which he is convinced they will – then the paper will be finished. He cannot and will not be responsible for that.

In any case, the paper would be seized by the authorities before it hit the streets if we were to make a demand like that.

His reservations are enough. At the moment. In a few days they could look like a lame excuse that robbed us of our last, tiny chance of survival.

The telephone lines are jammed with readers calling in. They are anxious, distraught, and they seem to place their last hopes in the paper. They tell us to prevent the Federal Republic from being dragged into this insane confrontation between the superpowers. 'Those people in Bonn' should be told clearly that the public does not want war. What are we supposed to say to those readers? We need help establishing our own sense of direction in all this.

The churches are filled to overflowing. There are crowds of people milling around in front of the Church of St Catherine in the Hauptwache because no more of them can fit into it. Prayers instead of resistance? Resignation instead of action?

The Council of the Evangelical Churches has warned those in power not to sin against humanity and creation and therefore against God. They need to realise, it says, that they are taking a grave burden of guilt on themselves if they push the confrontation any further. There are no justifications for a military confict, especially in Europe. And there is absolutely no reason why nuclear weapons should be used. The church calls on all Christendom to pray for God to help enlighten those who carry that grave responsibility, and fo. His grace to influence their decisions.

The Catholic Bishops' Conference has issued a statement that is equally naïve and removed from reality. The Holy Father is deeply concerned. All the faithful are called upon to join him in prayer and imprecation, for this is the time of need and of testing. God alone knows, the bishops say, why he has now allowed mankind to be visited with this harsh trial. His actions are inscrutable. This does not mean, however, that those in responsible political positions are not dutybound to reach their decisions in a spirit of brotherly love as expressed in the Sermon on the Mount – which means 'love thine enemy'. The Pope firmly condemns even the slightest thought of the use of nuclear weapons. This would be a terrible sin. May God help the rulers of His Church.

It is probably too late for that. Both churches have held firmly to their old watchword of 'making peace with or without weapons', despite desperate pleas from their grass-roots believers. Their policy has been to firmly condemn the actual use of nuclear weapons, but to adhere at the same time to the principle of deterrence, to which they have given their blessing 'temporarily' as a morally legitimate policy for 'securing the peace'. Once the 'temporary' period was over, the nuclear balance of fear was to be condemned as immoral. Fine. Except that the church never stipulated how long the 'temporary' period was to be.

Since when have questions of morality or immorality been tied to deadlines? Has that deadline run out now that developments in weapons technology have taken deterrence beyond the absurd? Not a single clear statement from the church's hierarchy about these things.

The mood in the office is like a Trappist monastery. Everyone working away alone and in silence, with a kind of grim determination. Fear is looking over our shoulders at our desks; it is with us as we write, sub articles.

I believe we're just infecting our readers with our own fear.

Tina called up just now. She told me that she loved me, and that nothing and no one will be able to destroy what there is between us. It did me good to hear her voice. She restores my courage.

How do women actually put up with this insane threat, which after all has been brought about by men? Erich Fromm's theory that human beings have an unconscious necrophiliac

22

urge inside them applies to only half the human race – the male half. The lust for death, for killing, for lethal risks, must be a purely male characteristic. Woman is more connected to life than man, and yet she takes little part in the way the world is shaped.

The patriarchal view has shaped our politics, history and society according to male ideals and values, which it has been prepared to defend to the death. The dualism in Freud's theory of human impulses does not apply to the human race in general. Rather it should read: for women, the impulse towards life is dominant, in men the impulse towards death.

Would female generals have sent millions of women to die in the hell of the First World War? Could women have bayoneted each other in their thousands, plunged steel into the bellies where life is nurtured and created? Would young girls be prepared to rush toward their deaths singing, as the troops did at Langemarck? Would women have been able to enthuse about 'a sweet and honourable death for the fatherland'?

One thing is for certain: patriarchy has subjected women and made them share its world view. Without the admiration of girls and women, the infantile notion of military heroism would have been unthinkable, and with it the entire value system of military life. It is girls and women who have always thrown flowers to departing and returning 'heroes' and who have obediently slaved away on the 'home front'.

But nevertheless, if the history of Europe had been dominated by women, there would probably have been no crusades, no witch trials, and the 'savages' in Africa, Asia and America would not have been slaughtered in their millions. A female Bonaparte? A female Hitler, Himmler, Eichmann? A female Stalin? Women such as Catherine the Great, Golda Meir, Indira Ghandi, Margaret Thatcher seem more like men in women's clothing.

In a matriarchal world, the kind of cold, planned, industrialised mass murder practised at Auschwitz would have been unthinkable, along with the concepts of 'master race' and 'sub-humans'. A woman would never have been able to write *Mein Kampf*, or give the order for the extermination of racial minorities that were 'unworthy of life'. In a matriarchy, a global slaughter such as occurred during the Second World War would have been inconceivable, as would labour camps, the liquidation of farmers, dissidents and 'enemies of the state'. A government dominated by women would never have been able to order the dropping of atomic bombs on Hiroshima and Nagasaki, and Japanese women would never have cut such a bloody swathe through South-East Asia. Female presidents and generals would not be able to torture and kill, or organise 'death-squads' to massacre human beings indiscriminately.

Weapons have 'fathers'. A man discovered gunpowder, the rifle, the canon, the machine-gun, the warplane, the atomic bomb, the hydrogen bomb, the missile, the multiple warhead. This absolutely perfect death machine, which is now capable of destroying all the higher forms of life on this planet, is the creation of male minds alone. It is men who are determined 'to turn the entire world into a desert bathed in poisonous mists with their idiotic threat that they will use their weapons "if they have to".' The 'moral and intellectual inadequacy' of which Thomas Mann wrote is a fault of the male.

28th July, evening

The Soviet newsagency said today that the Americans are mobilising in their bases in the Middle and Far East. The Soviet Union considers this a serious threat. Moscow will not be able to stand idly by while the Americans use those bases to create crisis flashpoints or even to open up new theatres of war.

This has to be seen as a scarcely-veiled threat. The only way that the USSR can prevent the Americans from threatening or attacking it from their 400 or so bases on Russia's borders is by using nuclear weapons. From a geostrategic point of view, the Kremlin is in the weaker position. It is surrounded. An opponent who has been pushed into a corner is liable to attack suddenly or to lash out irrationally. It is his only chance. Animals behave like that too; it is their instinctive way of operating. And it is precisely when the deterrent system demands more clear-headedness and predictability than ever – at a time like now, that is – that irrational emotions and anxiety-dictated reactions

24

start to gain the upper hand. But this means that there is no deterrent any more. The enemy who is surrounded and trapped is not being deterred – on the contrary, he is being pushed into some kind of action.

To ignore this simple but dangerous fact is sheer blindness.

It is hard to get any overview of the fighting. American bombers have been attacking Soviet troops in Ethiopia and the North Yemen – with success, UPI claims, and with severe losses, TASS emphasises. The White House has firmly rejected a Russian ultimatum demanding that it halt land operations on Cuba immediately. The air raids on the island are continuing. TASS talks of huge casualties among the Cuban civilian population, but American military sources deny this.

The political and military leaderships on both sides will be unable to keep control of military developments in these distant theatres of war for long, even though they could quickly combine into a general holocaust. No sign of either side becoming more reasonable. It seems increasingly certain that each of the superpowers is determined to gain a decisive victory – even if that means the other must back down. But to give way or become more conciliatory can only be interpreted as a surrender, according to the rules of the deterrent system. Nuclear deterrence allows no room for conciliation once a certain crisis threshold has been crossed. Then all that is left is the automatic escalation of military action.

All day I have been haunted by a childhood experience that I thought was long forgotten. It was in the summer of 1942, and I was visiting my grandparents. It was early evening; we were sitting at dinner. A summer storm erupted over the little village at the foot of the Carpathians. The thunder seemed to merge with the flashes of lightning, so close was the centre of the storm, but in grandpa's presence I felt no fear. Then a bolt of lightning hit the stables. The horses started to thrash and whinny in fear of their lives. Their neighing sounded more like screaming. There was a smell of burning. Grandpa rushed out, and no one noticed that I was behind him. I positioned myself under the covered gate leading to the stables. And then out galloped Janosik, my favourite horse. The black stallion rushed around

25

the broad square of the yard, with sparks flying from his hooves, splashing in puddles, his coat glistening in the rain. The animal's eyes were contorted with terror so that only the whites were visible. Panting hard, he made for the gate. Slowly, very slowly, the dark shape blacked out the sky from me. I raised my hand in front of me to protect myself from the violence racing towards me, and I did not feel the blow from Janosik's hoof.

Tina says that her department won't be working tomorrow. The entire factory will be taking part in the silent demonstration in the centre of Wiesbaden. The management has given its permission.

29th July, mid-day

The population is showing its first signs of panic. The nuclear threat has come closer to home and is now seen as a real danger to life. Too late? A volcano does not 'sleep'. It suddenly erupts and spits lava.

Long before Wiesbaden, roads were impassable. I left the car on a forest track near the North Cemetery and walked through the seething inner city to the main railway station.

The public's attitude is depressing but perhaps understandable. People are fighting, not against the danger, but for personal survival. Shops were literally under siege. Screaming and cursing, glassy-eyed, people were forcing their way through the mass of abandoned cars, clambering over vehicles and car bonnets. Many shops have been looted, stripped totally clean.

Hysteria had reached such a pitch that the psychological floodgates were opening. The staff of the Hertie department store were defending themselves in their shattered display windows with spraycans and iron bars. The smaller stores were locked and barred, little fortresses.

At the main station in Frankfurt, travellers were greeted with loudspeaker announcements: 'Avoid the inner city! You will not get any farther. Frankfurt has been cordoned off! Take the next train home!' Chaos. Bemused members of the public milling around, colliding with one another. Hundreds shoved onto the rails. A lot of casualties even here. Police at battalion strength on the square in front of the station and in the Münchnerstrasse and the Kaiserstrasse – even they could not gain access to the inner city, although they were setting about themselves ruthlessly with their truncheons, increasing the general panic. There were police helicopters landing on the roofs of the Dresdner Bank and the BFG Building. Trams stuck, cars bumper to bumper, their drivers pale and often in tears.

The surging, panting crowds have already stormed the banks on the Hauptwache. Some of their fear has given way to anger. They felt cheated when the banks ran out of money. The rush came too quickly for the financial institutions to cope.

When have we Germans ever lost our composure in a crisis like this? We even behaved in a disciplined way during the bombing raids in the last war.

Failed attempts by the police to address the crowds through a megaphone from the first storey of the Cafe Kranzler. Police cars and ambulances near the Katherinenkirche, lights flashing and sirens wailing, making no progress against the tide of humanity.

Horror as I trod on a yielding body underfoot. I had not seen it. Several people must have been trampled to death in the rush down the stairs to ground level. Indescribable scenes. Masses of humanity pushing up from the underground station, masses in headlong flight downwards. The result: people collapsing in seething heaps. Several lifeless bodies in the Uhren-Christ shopping arcade. No one paying any attention to them. Remnants of material and blood on the shattered panes of the display windows.

Reached the office, body pouring with sweat and on the edge of a nervous collapse.

A crisis committee is making every effort to co-ordinate things. Half of my colleagues are absent, only one copy boy is there, the telex has been deserted, and the telephone exchange is only half-manned. At this stage, no one knows whether we'll be able to produce a paper at all.

The same picture in other cities. Hundreds of shops, supermarkets and banks have been looted. The public has lost its head. All of us are scared of dying, and suddenly everyone

27

knows that he is a potential candidate for death, no matter where in this country he may try to flee.

How are they going to wage war with a population in this condition? But then these days they don't actually need the people in order to have their war. All they have to do is to put the lid on it for a few days. The military machine, in its splendid invulnerability, will arrange the rest automatically and alone.

The government has shown its usual sensitivity: it has unmasked 'Moscow's Fifth Column'. Apparently subversive, communist rabblerousers, schooled and trained in secret, have been responsible for creating and fomenting the mood of panic. The Federal Minister of the Interior has announced severe measures against subversion. If this occurred again, armed force would be used to restore order. This country would not permit its defensive capability to be undermined in this way. There would be no 'inner front'. The authorities knew not just the subversive elements but also their sympathisers and helpers. It was now evident that the government's long-suffering tolerance of the peace movement and 'organised pacifism' had been a fundamental mistake.

It seems to me to be something approaching a law of history that war only becomes possible when the political leadership of the country involved has become afflicted with a psychotic view of reality, a sort of partial blindness.

This stage has now been reached.

Despite everything, there is a resurgence of hope in the office. The riots have shown more effectively than any organised demonstration that the West German public wants peace. Peace at any price. It is neither ready nor willing to fight. It doesn't give a damn about military readiness, because it knows that the military options are closed ones. The government will simply have to take this fact into account.

If the crisis between the two superpowers can't be contained and threatens to spread to Europe, there will be general insurrection. Even the Americans will have to take the fact into account that the Europeans know they are sitting on a powderkeg. Late in the day perhaps, but possibly not too late.

What use are allies like these to Washington? At last it is becoming clear that people are not willing to accept the threat

28

of annihilation as some kind of a natural disaster – something which the politicians must have been counting on when they made their feasibility studies for a nuclear war in Europe. There are no rational grounds for war in Europe. No one wants to shoot, no one wants to march to war. There are no political conflicts that can only be solved by force. Europe – East or West – has no desire to be hostage to the world powers.

29th July, evening

The Soviet Union, the GDR and Czechoslovakia are accusing the West of fomenting trouble among their populations. Counter-revolutionary elements infiltrated from outside have been attempting, they say, to stir up mass panic in order to cripple the defensive readiness of the GDR and Czechoslovakia and to lure the masses away from fraternal solidarity with the peoples of the Soviet Union. Most of these have been identified and put out of harm's way, however. Such attempts are bound to fail.

Hopes faded quickly in the office after that.

Nevertheless, somehow we shall produce a newspaper tomorrow, though it will be much reduced in size. No advertisements any more, no small ads either. A pretty good indication of the public mood in itself.

The Federal Minister of the Interior has sent a telex telling the press that it must be mindful of its patriotic duty at this historic moment and support the call for calm. We won't mention it in tomorrow's paper.

Provisional casualty figures after today's mass panic: 27 dead in the inner city areas of Frankfurt and several hundred more or less seriously injured. Damage to property runs into millions. Tomorrow shops and banks will be closed – a temporary measure, official sources say.

I walked to the main station, for the city's train system had stopped functioning. Police at all 'strategically important points'. Teams of workers employed by the city are working frantically to clear away the evidence of mass terror. The authorities have obviously decided on a return to 'normality'.

It's all to be dismissed as a temporary aberration. The sort of unfortunate thing that can happen sometimes. They are probably mindful of the enemy: What will the Soviets think of us? Our defensive readiness must not be weakened either. But how can we be ready when no one wants to be?

Tina tells me that things have stayed quiet in Taunusrodt. We are both rather painfully determined not to show our own fear. When we are together, I find myself avoiding thinking about what a serious threat the world crisis poses to our private life together. We are both fighting the thought that our life together could be measured in no more than hours. To look at it another way, the fate of our relationship will mirror that of the earth. This connection of the personal with the global has a somewhat unreal quality.

30th July, mid-day

The Federal Government and the Federal Parliament have put a section of the emergency laws into operation. Airports and border crossings are closed with immediate effect, and only foreigners can leave the country. Switzerland and France in particular, but also Austria and the Benelux countries, have been pressing for this measure, the government says. Quite understandable! From the point of view of the French, we have 'been chosen as the nuclear battlefield in a future war, for both historical and geographical reasons'. The French socialists, who actually expressed this elementary truth in their electoral manifesto some years ago, were being more realistic than any German governments. The former American Defence Secretary, Weinberger, said much the same. Bonn should have been listening more closely, paid more attention to our allies' opinions so as to get a clearer idea of our actual chances of defending ourselves . . .

Instead of sticking our heads in the sand. Now that we Germans have realised what the Americans and the French have always known, we're having the door shut on us so that we don't infect the French and the others with our terror. So far as our allies are concerned, we're suddenly outcasts. Undesirables.

Will the French authorities send back Christine and Ralf? If the pair of them know what they are doing, they will stay in Antibes as long as they can.

The forces of order in Wiesbaden also have the situation 'under control' today. The first road blocks on the highways into the city, also at the main station and surrounding the inner city. Banks and supermarkets have been put under guard, and there are police patrols everywhere. 'Normality' is being emphasised, damaged cars towed away and display windows replaced with new glass.

But the atmosphere of fear and anxiety is still there, a tangible force. Only a few people on the streets, very few drivers. Repeated appeals on the radio for people to go to work. Absence from work without proper excuse will be viewed as refusal and penalised accordingly. But it is impossible to ignore the fact that this country has suffered a collapse. Its life blood has ceased to circulate properly.

The trains are running on time again, but they are empty. The few passengers sit far apart and alone in the free seats, from force of habit.

The Social Democrats have shown their usual ability to be 'responsible' in the country's hour of need: they have given their assent to the partial activation of the emergency laws and have made a demand for an all-party coalition. This has come to nothing, however, because the Greens' parliamentary group has categorically rejected the idea and has announced a policy of total resistance instead. We are faced with the threat of a constitutional conflict.

German Social Democracy and the trade union movement have failed us in this historic moment as they have so often before. And now, when the existence of the German nation is in the balance, we have to ask ourselves if such a failure not only robs our labour movement of its meaning but even makes it co-responsible for the series of German catastrophes that have scarred this century. The Social Democrats and the trade unions share responsibility for instilling a sense of social discipline in the workforce, and also for robbing it to a large extent of any sense of real participation in the shaping of our society. Above all, they have taken away the working class's will and ability to act in accordance with its most fundamental interests and to say a firm 'No!' to war.

The failure of German socialism to fulfil its historic role began long before the First World War. The fact that the sons of workers marched off to that war with just as much enthusiasm as the sons of the middle classes, ready and willing to plunge bayonets into the guts of French workers, is just one piece of evidence of that failure. The leadership of the Social Democratic Party knew full well that it would have been more of a patriotic act to refuse war credits in that fatal August of 1914. The trade union bosses knew that a general strike would have been a patriotic act. They would have done inestimable service to international solidarity – with enormous consequences for the future of Europe. There would have been no Second World War, and our present world would naturally have been quite different. At this moment in history, the two superpowers are presenting a bill that has been left unpaid since 1945.

Basically, the Social Democratic Party has collapsed when faced with the problem of combining theory with practice. 'The next European war will be a game with no limits such as the world has never seen, according to all indications the last-ever war. All who have any understanding of the world know this; only governments do not seem to realise it, or they would stop playing with fire. They are moving along the road to ruin, as if driven by invisible forces of destruction.' Thus the words of the Social Democratic Parliamentary Delegation to the Reichstag in 1911.

And only a few years ago the praesidium of the Social Democratic Party stated: 'The Social Democratic Party lends its voice to those who fear that another war will certainly be the last one. Any responsible approach to defence policy must take into account the fact that once deterrence has failed, there is a high level of probability that the use of nuclear weapons will be inevitable. Those in government in East and West seem to be the only people who do not take this fully into account, or they would stop playing with fire. The arms race is not some accident of nature that must inevitably lead us to destruction.'

The government and the authorities were caught completely by surprise by yesterday's developments. Public statements now call for us to trust the government, which is in constant, close communication with allied governments.

This is all very well, but it would be equally important to be in communication with the Soviet government and the governments of the Warsaw Pact countries. But the channels of communication between East and West have obviously broken down. All that is left is ultimatums and threats, and beyond those only military action.

In the office we are trying to find out when the restrictive measures detailed in the emergency laws – food rationing, petrol rationing, the authority to requisition private vehicles – will be enforced. We have been told that there is no question of these powers being used for the moment.

There have been rumours that monetary restrictions are about to be introduced, to prevent a price explosion when the shops re-open tomorrow. Our good burghers will certainly plunder their savings accounts. How will they come to terms with this new experience – that from tomorrow money, previously our society's all-powerful instrument, will be of limited use? Will they also realise that even money can't buy an extra chance of survival?

The rapidly escalating threat of extinction has suddenly made us all equal. But equality in the face of catastrophe is not especially comforting. On board the *Titanic*, when it was a matter of sheer survival, everyone was also equal, millionaires and poor immigrants alike. They were all – literally – in the same boat. Now all of us, in Germany, in East and West Europe, and probably the entire human race, are in the same boat. Friend, foe, and neutral. The threat is the same for all of us. If one of us drowns, we will drag the other with us. The politicians and the military men haven't understood that.

30th July, evening

Every time I feel a resurgence of hope, even if it is no more than a grabbing after straws, I find myself plunged back into gloom by the government's public statements. The Federal Minister of Defence has told his fellow citizens why he is still confident: the

33

deterrent effect of strategic nuclear weapons will hold both the superpowers back from the ultimate recourse. These weapons mark the limits beyond which neither power will go.

It is hopeless! Even at this stage, the citizens of this country are being treated like idiots by their leaders, as they have been for decades past. The deterrent effect of intercontinental missiles is irrelevant so far as Germany and Europe are concerned; it is precisely because of the fears they arouse in the Russians and the Americans that the two superpowers will be tempted to wage a relatively low-risk tactical nuclear war in Europe. Is it a question of deliberate deception, aimed at keeping the public quiet, or is it simple intellectual inadequacy that enables the politicians and the military men to make this – for us – absurd distinction between tactical and strategic nuclear weapons? This distinction makes sense only for the Russians and the Americans. For Europe, even a tactical nuclear war will be the end. Whether or not the superpowers then choose to fight it out with strategic weapons will be of no concern to us, for Europe will already have been turned into a radioactive, lifeless wasteland.

What basis is there for us in history to trust the military? In 1914 they totally ignored the strategic significance of the machine gun, even though they had had decades in which to study the use of this weapon in manoeuvres. Instead, they ordered the same 'glorious' frontal attacks that had been used in 1870–71 during the Franco-Prussian War. Army Corps after Army Corps was sent to its futile destruction. In 1939, most generals were unaware of the significance of the tank and the tactical bomber. The Poles put their faith in their cavalry, the French trusted their Maginot Line.

It is obvious that today's military commanders are haunted by their experiences in the last world war. They believe that they can stage tank and air battles as they did in 1939–45 – much more effectively, at higher speed, and with greater precision, but in principle the same kind of warfare. But once a few hundred tactical nuclear weapons have managed to destroy a division at the push of a button, there will be no chance of 'having the capability of leading troops in the face of nuclear fire'. A grotesque denial of reality.

What grounds remain for hope? I fear that we are basing ours

34

on the ultimate weapon of self-defence available to the human psyche: a condemned man's refusal to accept imminent extinction, because the idea seems an absurdity. Anything that lies beyond our experience and understanding seems absurd.

Only now is the absurdity of a global nuclear war being fully understood, because the first steps towards it have already been taken. When, if not now, will we realise that the next step could be the decisive and final one? Now of all times, reason – that capacity to look into the abyss and see that it leaves no options for any of us – must deter both sides from any further escalation.

It is the hope based on 'it-can't-be-true', the hope to which the condemned man clings even as he is being led to the place of execution. His situation seems absurd, and so he hopes that the executioner will read out, not the death warrant but a free pardon. The United Nations Security Council has been in permanent session since today. Mutual, blinkered statements of blame by each of the superpowers and their hangers-on. The desire for confrontation is clear.

The neutral and Third World countries have finally realised that their survival is also at stake. A global nuclear war would also mean the end for them. India's representative has pointed out the grotesque quality of what is happening: two-fifths of the human race lives in countries affiliated either to the Warsaw Pact or NATO. If these nations – which now seems possible despite the situation's inherent unreality – use just half their stockpiles of nuclear weapons against each other, then the rest of humanity, the other three-fifths, will be condemned to destruction along with them – or at least to a dramatic deterioration in its quality of life. The attitude of the NATO and Warsaw Pact governments is thus totally irresponsible. Any further escalation can only be seen as criminal.

The USA has been instructed to withdraw from Cuba and conclude its ground operations there and in Saudi Arabia. In return, the Soviets are to give up their military bases in Ethiopia and North Yemen and to halt their massing of forces in the Far East.

The UN has offered help: UN troops will be stationed in the disputed areas.

I have a feeling – one that is rapidly turning into a certainty – that we are watching the unfolding of a classic Greek tragedy. Everyone is behaving as if the actors were speaking and behaving rationally, whereas in fact they are merely moving themselves and the rest of us towards some predetermined fate. We are not even to be granted the illusory consolation of asking questions about guilt and responsibility.

If global nuclear war has really been inevitable all along, it would have been better if it had happened twenty or thirty years ago, as a result of the Cuba Crisis or a similar conflict. Then we should still have stood a chance of survival. Since then, the chances have lessened from year to year.

More demonstrations this afternoon across the country, in most cities and outside military installations. The police and the Federal Border Security Force reacted with the utmost severity. The army was used in München, Stuttgart, and Hanover. Attempts by the public in East Hesse to blockade nuclear stockpile sites, munitions depots and barracks were squashed quickly.

The Federal Government and the American military authorities have announced that the military and police units concerned will shoot to disable and kill if such incidents are repeated. The threat has since been broadcast several times on radio and television. There have been many injuries and arrests. The people who live near nuclear power stations are also showing signs of anxiety. Protest meetings have demanded the shutting down of reactors for the duration of the international crisis. The government has refused.

What good is it talking about a country's 'defensive capability' when by firing three or at most four missiles at live reactors, an enemy can turn the Federal Republic into a radioactive wasteland? What a contradiction! We have spent years crediting the 'enemy' with all kinds of evil intentions, but in wartime we have to rely on his not exploiting such obvious military advantages.

According to the latest statement from NATO headquarters in Brussels, mobilisation is 'not being considered at this stage', so long as the Warsaw Pact doesn't mobilise. There is, of course, 'creeping mobilisation' underway in the East according to

36

NATO. And the spokesmen for the Warsaw Pact are making just the same accusation about the West . . . Despite the 'ominous situation which has been created in such an irresponsible manner', each side is claiming that it is being careful to avoid any confrontation in Europe. A NATO spokesman: *The responsibility is not ours, but the Kremlin's.* A Warsaw Pact spokesman: *The responsibility is not ours, but belongs to the leaders of NATO.*

When it really comes down to it, despite the flood of news items, we journalists have no idea what is going on. While we sit at our desks and try to hide our fear and our helplessness, somewhere far above us, spy satelites are checking whether the other side's intercontinental missiles are being prepared for use. That is what our fate really hangs on – and, in particular, how the satellite information is interpreted in Moscow and Washington.

Whether there will be a nuclear war in Europe is totally dependent on how the military commanders and politicians on both sides gauge each other's possible goals. If, at this moment, just a handful of powerful men lose their nerve, because someone interprets or presents the information wrongly! Or because the satellite itself provides false information! We can only wait, hope, and – if we are still capable of it – pray.

Any confidence in the manageability of this crisis and of the extraordinarily complex military apparatus involved would only be justified if there were no chance that this handful of men could be wrong in any decision they make. Mistakes are out of the question, or the entire powderkeg will go sky-high! And if they are wrong, they can only make their preparations according to agreed procedures, which will in turn be based on pre-agreed scenarios. And those scenarios will have to be accurate as well. Once the fighting starts in this day and age, there is no room for improvisation, to say nothing of generalship.

In the Second World War, commanders still had weeks or even months for reconnaissance, for rehearsal, developing and carrying through military operations. Today the time allowed has shrunk to hours or even minutes. Once the military machine is in motion, there is no room for individual judgements or decisions or modifications. War in Europe will be a nuclear war, and it will develop with bewildering speed. The modern

37

military machine only functions if, once the starting signal has been given, the politicians and the commanders give up all control and take no further part in the process. A terrifying thought.

It is clear from the mid-day news that the entire world has been gripped by fear. Demonstrations and protests in all European countries, including in the Eastern Bloc. The Storting was stormed in Oslo. Hardly anyone is going into work. Militiamen have used extreme brutality against striking workers in Hungary and Poland. In Krakow, participants in a demonstration by women and mothers were beaten up. To all intents and purposes, Europe is in a state of general strike. Fear is fomenting global solidarity. The people of Europe don't want war. This is our hope, and those in responsible positions must realise it too.

It is also possible, of course, that these worldwide mass protests will actually cause them to set their war machines in motion sooner – before their own people can strip them of their power. Those in authority now have to deal, not only with the 'enemy' but with their own people. A real two-front war.

The government spokesman in Bonn has given an assurance that the Americans have 'not yet' readied the 250 Pershing II missiles and the 800 cruise missiles stationed in Europe. Such a step, he said, would only be taken after the closest consultation with allied governments. No one believes him. Will the Soviets believe him? The Americans will do as they see fit, and NATO will have no say in it, let alone the Bundeswehr's high command.

The spectre of catastrophe is everywhere. Every evening I drag my fear back with me to these four walls. If only I could stop thinking about the future all the time, suffering doubly in anticipation. I feel as if I have some fatal disease in my body. Tina's presence, her warmth and her aliveness, mitigates the violence of these feelings. From now on, our two destinies are wholly connected.

31st July, Saturday, 12 noon

People are angry and outraged. Cheques are frequently being refused and only accepted if the customer is known to the shopkeeper. The centre of Wiesbaden is nevertheless a hive of hectic

38

activity. People buying everything they can lay their hands on. But there are also some depressingly violent and aggressive scenes.

Little groups of demonstrators carrying placards mingle with the anxious crowds. The first prophets of doom and preachers of Armaggedon are starting to make their presence felt. But somehow they lack a certain magic and capacity to shock. Foretelling catastrophe doesn't require much art these days.

The forces of order are staying in the background. If they succeed in isolating people and making them so insecure that they can think only of themselves and their own survival, then the masses will be manageable. Fear will make everyone retreat into their own homes like snails. Any mass consciousness must be discouraged. This is obviously the authorities' strategy. The desire for survival is to be encouraged – at the expense of the desire for life itself.

31st July, evening

Despite the fact that it is Saturday, work at the paper. A special edition and a Sunday paper. The public are buying papers as fast as we can print them. They are looking for some tiny glimmer of hope in the news and the comments. We are being forced to disappoint them: there is only rising tension, an increasing danger of war. Neither side is giving an inch. We can only report that all governments are afraid that the conflict will spread.

The President of France takes the view that there are no rational grounds for war in Europe. But how can we explain to our readers that the reason why war is possible is precisely because nuclear threat and counterthreat have lost their deterrent effects, and so grounds for war now exist?

In the afternoon, breathless phone calls from various correspondents: several country roads in the area between Heilbronn, Schwäbisch Gmund and Ulm have been closed to normal traffic. American soldiers and Bundeswehr units are turning all private vehicles back. Only the major highways have been left open to traffic. No details have been given, except that the measures are 'temporary'.

The situation is obvious: the Americans have armed their nuclear missiles. Since earlier today, the Pershings have been primed and have been travelling along pre-planned routes to their launch pads, ready for firing as soon as the order is given. The government spokesman must either have been lying or have been misinformed.

To find out whether the cruise missiles stationed in the Eifel are being prepared for launch, we simply ring up ordinary householders in Brandscheid and Neuerburg. Immediate confirmation: entire stretches of road have been blocked, cutting off whole districts.

Another shock. After how many in the last few days? The unthinkable – until now still diffuse and abstract, a theoretical sense of threat and danger to our lives – has suddenly become very concrete and conceivable. Charlie Lang asks dully: 'Do you think the Russians know what's happening?' The fear is so intense I can hardly breathe. By now, at the very latest, the Russians will be readying their own missiles for firing.

The Kremlin leadership and the Soviet generals will never allow a single Pershing or even Cruise Missile to strike a target in the Soviet Union. The leadership could never afford a failure on that scale, especially as it possesses the means to counter that danger. If the Russians come to the conclusion that the Americans are in earnest, they will attack first, as a preventive measure, to cover their flank in the West. From their standpoint, they have no other real choice. It would be enough, actually, for just one side to believe that they have no choice any more but were acting under pressure of circumstances.

They can have no doubt about the Americans' aims. Decapitation has been a consistent threat now for years. And the Pershings and the Cruise Missiles have been vaunted as the executioner's axe. But when the counterstrike comes, it will not hit the executioner but his assistant, who is actually carrying the axe. Which means us.

What a crazy policy successive German governments have followed – almost criminal in its short-sightedness – by supporting a strategy that provokes an over-powerful enemy into a first strike!

Editorial conference. The majority is again in favour of our making an appeal for resistance, and by a very large margin: at this stage, a collective refusal to go along with this insanity is our only chance. We must not allow ourselves to be deflected from our duty by the government's reaction, which will be predictable. Perhaps we can give a signal. We know that others working in newspapers, as well as in radio stations and television studios, feel the same and have a similar level of commitment.

Those armed American missiles will draw a Soviet nuclear strike onto us like lightning conductors, and it won't matter whether it is a first strike or a retaliation. In either case, the Federal Republic will be a defenceless target. The Americans have no right to extend their armed confrontation with the Soviets into Europe. For Europe, the risk is no longer acceptable. Anyone who is in any position at all to oppose this berserk military machine is duty bound to resist.

The Soviets are frightened of the Pershings. But rather than paralyse them, this fear will goad them into ruthless action. It is foolish to assume that the Russians will stay within the limits of the scenario that NATO has projected for this situation. There will be no conventional attack; instead there will be a nuclear strike. Everything else is wishful thinking, illusions.

If, on the other hand, the people could be successfully called on to resist . . .

And what form would the resistence take, colleagues are asking.

Yes. How would it be? Demonstrations, appeals? Warnings? Blockades? A general strike? A vast exercise in passive resistance?

These dry, objective questions show exactly how helpless we really are.

Yes: general strike, blockades. Resistance may be 'utopian', but then the threat of the inferno is no longer unreal either. It is only too real. The people must block the roads leading eastward in their hundreds of thousands, so that the troops cannot move through to the 'front', and they must swamp the launch sites at the Pershing bases, so that the missiles cannot be fired. People in the Soviet Union are frightened too, as they are in the GDR, in Czechoslovakia, Hungary and Poland; in all probability they are waiting for the signal that will inspire them to do the same. When all is said, people over there must know that they can't

41

defend themselves by military means either. The GDR's National People's Army has become just as pointless as our Bundeswehr. To resist is our duty and our moral responsibility. Above all, it is our last chance – even though it may just be an ethical principle.

We end up once again with no decision, no call for resistance. Instead the formula says that we 'critically distance ourselves' from the government's defence policy. This is too feeble. We shall do our duty to the last. But which duty? As some of us watch the last chance disappearing, the others grasp at straws.

The Pershings and Cruise Missiles that are now ready and primed in the Swabian Alp and the Eifel are strategic weapons, others in the office argue, as if they are trying to persuade themselves of something. The Americans must realise that they will be starting a strategic war if they use them. The Soviets realise it too. The government in Washington can't be so stupid that it will abandon all the other military and political options still available short of the strategic threshold and threaten immediate strategic war, which would mean its own national suicide. The Soviets can rely on the fact that the US government is not made up of suicides, and the same applies in reverse.

To argue in this way is only possible if some kind of psychic block is in operation, preventing any appreciation of the real danger. Many animals do this. When they are faced with a deadly, inescapable danger, they begin to clean themselves or to hop and jump around as if dancing for joy.

We part, feeling at the mercy of God.

According to Max Born, technological progress has outstripped mankind's moral capacity, and Einstein maintained that it was beyond our intellectual and organisational abilities as well. For years now it has been clear that all our forms of government, democratic and authoritarian alike, have been under great strain, trying to cope with the consequences of a technological revolution that has mushroomed into a global threat; the often irreversible destruction of the environment, the inhospitable and often inhumane nature of modern societies, the hopeless situation of the masses in the Third World, the absoluteness of the destructive power vested in modern nuclear weapons. All these problems have created irreversible factors in the world that even at best would be only partially correctable.

Our destructive capabilities cannot be wished away. They remain a fact. But science and technology are still nowhere near the limits of their potential. Their potential is in the realm of the utopian. Such a Utopia would provide political decision making frameworks that permitted human beings to decide on issues that resulted from the breakneck pace of developments. The system of representative decision making, whether democratic or by usurpation, has reached its limits and has failed. If the general public had been able to decide, the arms race would never have exploded into the infinite as it has. If the public had been able to decide, there would have been no military confrontation and no imminent danger of mankind's extinction. The people, of whichever countries, do not want war, and neither do their representatives, but they are incapable of stopping it. Technology is their master.

This is why we should tell the people now: Take your fate in your own hands! You have no other choice if you want to survive! Your rulers have failed! There are only seconds to midnight. The entire human race is facing the abyss. The military apparatuses that have been set in motion are working together in unison, like one big doomsday machine. Those in power cannot stop them, even if they want to. They are their prisoners. Only the masses can do it. Each individual must be prepared to be a grain of sand, so that together we can throw ourselves into the works of this perfect, automatically functioning machine and stop it!

But is collective sanity still a practical possibility?

31st July, midnight

Walking to the station late in the evening. Frankfurt was like a ghost town. The Kaiserstrasse looked as though there had been an enormous police raid: no whores, no pimps, no 'clients', no sightseers, no foreigners. The bright neon lights usually outside the peepshows, the cabarets and cinemas have been switched off. An Omen? I suddenly missed the disreputable, ambivalent,

43

vulgar and to some extent brutal – but very much alive – atmosphere of the place. Has our so-called demi-monde a finer sense of danger than the disciplined average citizen? The city seemed to be waiting, holding its breath as if expecting a tornado.

The danger is invisible but omnipresent. It may have its home thousands of kilometres away in concrete bunkers or on huge launching pads, but there are no limits to where it can go, no walls, no defence and no protection. It is there, like the air. I try to imagine a real comparison: perhaps it is as if each of us carried a pistol mounted on the nape of our necks, which will be fired when someone gives the order, or as if everyone, from babes in arms to centenarians, walked around with a rope round their necks, which would pull them off the ground and throttle them when the same order was given.

In the old days, we could see the danger, decide our attitude to it, choose between fighting or fleeing. It was apparent in the form of marching enemy soldiers. In a comparable situation in Frankfurt during the Middle Ages, the city would have been filled with hectic but purposeful activity. The city would have been preparing itself for a siege and organising its defence. They would have been opening the arsenals and handing out weapons, stationing men on the walls, filling the provisions stores, driving cattle in from outside. The city would have girded its loins, and all its citizens would have been involved, for each would have had his contribution to make – even the wastrel, raising morale by his mockery of the enemy. To be prepared to defend yourself, and to be determined to do so, was sensible, and boldness and courage also had their purpose. The defenders knew why they were preparing to sacrifice their lives. They had a real chance. Fear did not paralyse those burghers; instead it urged them on to feats of exertion.

And if all this was of no avail, and the city fell, then it was possible to appeal to the victor's generosity. Even if the city was razed to the ground, it could be rebuilt. No matter how cruel the victor might be in his fury, no matter what horrors there were to endure, many, indeed most, of the inhabitants would survive.

Now the city was simply helpless and defenceless. An easy, and a large target. A beacon to the enemy. And the enemy is neither cruel nor kind, he is nowhere in sight. He is a handful of elderly gentlemen who are afraid, and a few generals who have lost control of their machine, and a few cool missile specialists, who will turn the key that launches the weapons of destruction.

This enemy will act according to the laws and pressures forced on him by modern weapons technology. If the computers follow the pre-programmed list of targets and reach the inbuilt escalation level necessary to launch a missile against Frankfurt, this order will be carried out as a purely technical operation, relatively without passion or feeling. It will be a problem simply of technical and military efficiency. The inferno that will descend on the city within seconds – literally out of a clear blue sky – will be registered by the military technicians in the Soviet Union only inasmuch as the red, blinking light that represented the living Frankfurt on their electronic map will turn into a constant green light. And the target count register will have changed, nothing more.

Modern nuclear war does not even allow the enemy to beg for his life. No mother can hold out her child imploringly. Computers – unlike even the cruellest conqueror – have no hearts.

I find myself filled with hatred, reinforced by a sense of total helplessness, at the idiocy, this blinkered stupidity, this coldness, this easy willingness to commit a crime of global proportions, one that will take just hours to exceed all others in human history a hundred thousandfold.

Took sleeping tablets for the first time. Not just to sleep, but to keep away these nightmares.

1st August, mid-day

Live reports from overflowing churches on the radio and television. People are looking for the meaning of existence in the houses of God. A return to God, to the idea of a kindly father who won't allow bullets or missiles to be fired. Naïve, but maybe comforting. An aid to life, or a comfort to the dying?

I have a distinct suspicion that the church services have been selected according to the 'positive' tendencies of the preachers. On the ARD channel, the Protestant military bishop is giving

45

the sermon, while on ZDF – by way of contrast – we have his Catholic counterpart. They are telling us to trust the government, which is under God's protection. In this grave hour, freedom and human dignity are in the balance. God, they say, is still the master of history. Nothing happens unless He wills it, even though His will is sometimes beyond our understanding. Prayer can have a power far beyond all dangers visited upon us by human will alone. We must obey the human authority there is God-given. All authority comes from God.

If the two reverend gentlemen had bothered to think things through, it might have occurred to them that this also applied to the Soviet government. God must have it under his protection too. Unfortunately these two God-given authorities are in conflict. And since people must obey authority, they are also in conflict and have become enemies, even though they don't want to be enemies at all.

As Heinrich Heine said, it is the old heavenly hocus-pocus, which is used to lull the people to sleep, which treats the people like a big lout who has to be quietened before he causes trouble.

The parson in little Taunusrodt, on the other hand, calls the present politics of confrontation, which knowingly risks an apocalypse of biblical proportions, nothing more than a crime. Christians are now called on to give their obedience to God rather than to Man. Those in power have taken a wrong path that leads away from God and Man like. Christians must now resist, because Christ died on the cross not for death but for life. Weigand, the parson, was always a courageous man, active in the peace movement. This also has something to do with the fact that he has been dumped here in this hick parish.

My neighbour, Thönnessen, has begun to dig a deep pit in his garden, three metres long, two metres across, two metres deep. It is to be an emergency shelter, he tells me, wiping the perspiration from his brow. He has read a pamphlet put out by the German Self-Defence Association, which says these kind of shelters are very effective in case of nuclear attack, if you pile plenty of earth on top of them. At least you don't end up being squashed under your own four walls. His two sons seem to view the whole thing as a waste of time. They spend a lot of time muttering disapprovingly in the background.

46

Lunch with Tina on the terrace. A warm day with blue skies. The sun is white-hot above the tablelands, and its light flitters through the trees. The birch trees are shivering gently, even though there is no breeze. Quiet, a summer siesta. I breath deep and easy, let my mind rest, my nerves to relax. The only sound, way among the yellow fields stretching beyond the village, is the throb of a combine harvester.

But I can still sense a deep unease, even in Tina. Because of the demonstration this afternoon? I don't feel good about it. I am going to drive over to the Erbenheim helicopter base.

1st August, evening

This is civil war. By which I mean war against civilians! Terror, with the full complicity of the occupying power. The state is mobilising against its own citizens, with a barbaric ruthlessness. Attempts by 25,000 citizens of Wiesbaden to demonstrate outside the Erbenheim base were shot to pieces. The German police tried to halt the protest procession by blocking the roads, but the crowds poured over into the meadows and fields.

Thousands came from the direction of Mainz-Kastel. A hundred metres from the barbed wire, the first shots were fired. At least three companies of American soldiers were standing around the perimeter and firing into the crowd with automatic rifles, without stopping. I thought, they'll not let anyone leave alive. Before the jostling, bewildered masses realised it, five helicopters were overhead, firing down on them. Those hit were spun around by the impact of the shots before they collapsed to the ground. The mesh fence flapped bizarrely in the hail of bullets, and the burst of fire kept whistling into the throng on the outside of the fence. After a minute or so, the nightmare was over, but as the crowds poured back in retreat, they ran into the rifles and clubs of the German police.

89 dead, more than 400 injured, of whom many will not survive.

The demonstration outside Frankfurt airport was also shot to pieces, as were the protests in Ramstein, Bitburg, Nörvenich, Jever, Mutlangen. It is impossible to draw up an accurate

47

casualty list. The radio and television are calling urgently for blood donors.

The Federal Chancellor speaks of a 'tragedy'. He says that he is personally very disturbed, but that the German security forces and our American friends had no choice. After all, the demonstrations had been banned.

He claims that there is evidence that the military bases were to have been taken outright by storm. The crowds had been led by communist subversives and trained saboteurs whose aim had been to create chaos, so that we would fall easy victims to the enemy. This could not be, and would not be, acceptable to the authorities. The Minister of the Interior had warned the nation on Friday, as a result of previous disturbances, that if such events were repeated firearms would be used. Our defensive capability had to be preserved at all costs.

I was trembling with fear and helpless rage for hours afterwards – like a man in a fever. Incapable of speech, feeling a terrible pressure to scream out loud. If only there were a chance of revenge! These awful scenes, the cold brutality. The helpless gestures of the bullet-riddled victims. A few were actually leaping about in the air, like hares being driven out of cover for the hunt.

An elderly man near me suddenly began to tip forwards, as if he had stumbled. A burst of automatic fire had torn away half his head, and the blood was fountaining out of the wound, but somehow he kept moving.

If the government believes in 'communist saboteurs', then it is a convenient self-deception, the kind of thing that can be used to justify any atrocity. Or paranoia! People in this country are afraid for their lives. They don't want to die in a nuclear war. That is the 'secret' of these demonstrations, and of resistance.

The Chancellor also announces that from Tuesday the emergency laws will be enforced in their entirety. A state of emergency will be defined according to the letter of the law.

So. From tomorrow the army has permission to shoot us.

1st August, midnight

From tomorrow, everything changes. The people's trust of the authorities has finally gone. A scream of outrage will and must come. Today's victims will not have died in vain if they have made their contribution towards averting the nuclear inferno. Their blood must not be allowed to have flowed in vain. Never before in history have human beings died for a more just cause: the continued existence of humanity. How can we get to grip with the absolute quality of the perspectives and dimensions created by the threat of nuclear annihilation? To die so that humanity may survive! Words fail me.

My nerves are shot. I am shivering with anxiety. I feel like vomiting. I hold on to Tina. And she could do with some support herself.

Almost mechanically I register that the Soviets have invaded Iran and Pakistan. Japan has mobilised. The NATO naval forces have closed the entrances to the Baltic and the Arctic Ocean. *Big Lift*, the air bridge from the USA to Europe, is in full operation.

The earth is ablaze from pole to pole. It is as if the firefighters are using petrol to put it out.

2nd August, mid-day

Yesterday's Bloody Sunday seems like a nightmare, but the speed of events robs it of its potential effects. What is happening at this moment is paralysing, doesn't allow the individual to breathe, is a violent, apparently endless terror. What happened yesterday is not important. The future is shrinking, becoming vague and dark.

The 1016 demonstrators who died for peace outside thirty-six military bases in the Federal Republic, died in vain. Today they are almost forgotten. Everyone is concerned with his private needs. A few half-hearted commentaries on the massacre in the press and radio this morning, most of them full of understanding for the actions of the Americans and the police. Hard, they say, but considering the threat from the East, fair. Our

49

defence capability must be preserved, etc. All those demonstrators must have realised the risk they were running, they had been warned. Journalistic cowardice. Thirty-six items of local news.

Our foreign 'guest workers' are now rushing to get home, as if to order, but this time the exodus is voluntary. The great exodus from 'the unsinkable aircraft carrier that is West Germany' has begun. Chaos in the cities, at the airports and on the roads. I took four hours to get to Frankfurt. Some trains stopped hundreds of metres from the station, stayed stuck there. The foreign workers have obviously not realised that the Rhein-Main airport has been closed to civilian traffic. American military transport aircraft are landing and taking off around the clock. The controversial building of the western runway can now be seen as an act of prophetic genius.

Desperate railway officials, screaming children, cursing adults, mountains of luggage. Bitter, sometimes aggressive comments from German passers-by. Suddenly the foreigners are being blamed for clearing off – and willingly, at that. These days it seems like desertion and ingratitude. We are beginning to feel that we have been left alone.

But then I would also feel a bit better if I were in Sicily or Andalusia right now!

The Federal Government has set up airlifts from Stuttgart, Nuremburg, Düsseldorf, Cologne, Hannover and Hamburg to Spain, Portugal and Italy. And 400 special trains have been laid on. Turkey alone is refusing to take in its own citizens. This coming Wednesday, the autobahns are to be kept free for any foreigners who wish to leave. The Federal Government is suddenly in a hurry to get rid of the foreign workers.

One piece of the jigsaw after another. The picture is forming inexorably: and it adds up to a big, black nothing.

In the concourse under the Hauptwache, the same bearded, bald violinist was there who has been giving virtuoso busking performances for years. Bach and Beethoven. As usual, his accompaniment came from a cassette recorder. As if nothing untoward had happened. The sight moved me very deeply. The hectic activity around the train and subway stations, constantly swallowing and spewing out humanity, the tension in the air, lent his playing an unreal quality. He just played, as if what was happening in the rest of the world had nothing to do with him. Kids were hanging around him in a semi-circle, drinking and smoking. Despite everything, music is very much a part of life.

2nd August, evening

The 'top ten thousand' are starting to leave along with the foreign workers. Main destination of the private jets is North Africa, but the French and the Swiss are also turning a blind eye and allowing rich Germans to fly into their countries, while refugees in cars are being turned back at the borders. Intriguing, but hardly suprising: the cream of the major publishers are also playing it safe and making themselves scarce, while their newspapers and magazines urge the masses to take courage and sweat it out.

What arouses particular (impotent) rage is the fact that several private planes have been able to take off from the Rhine-Main airport, despite the apparent ban on civil air traffic. Bribery, or a secret deal with the government? I suppose that on the other hand, after the holocaust we are going to need 'an elite that can function immediately it is required'.

Title of our reader article: *The Rats Are Leaving the Sinking Ship*. The rats – who have a very well-developed nose for what's happening – won't mind much what we say, and 'afterwards' things will be quite different anyway.

Total collapse on the stock market. Shares in German firms are for sale for small change, entire factories can be had for a few thousand marks. Apart from a few unrealistic optimists – or black humourists – no one wants them. I decide to buy some shares tomorrow. I decide to become a war profiteer.

There have been regular battles between police and German refugees on the French and Swiss borders. The French and Swiss security forces have used firearms. Specially-adapted helicopters are being sent over the border areas at night to hunt down any Germans trying to sneak across illegally under cover of darkness. It is hard to remember that NATO has not even officially mobilised yet, and that there has as yet been no cause for conflict. European solidarity!

51

I wonder whether the Soviets are also driving back refugees from their sister states, from Poland or Czechoslovakia, and shooting to kill?

Our local reporter from Eastern Hesse tells of hectic activity outside the American and German munitions depots in the area. The stores where tactical warheads are kept have obviously been emptied. Ready to start! No one knows if it will be the Soviets or the Americans who take the next step on the ladder of escalation, who is ahead and who behind at the moment.

What useful job can we journalists do these days? What good is information? Do ever more dramatic reports of new catastrophes actually give the reader any kind of real guidance? For what? How? Do they help the individual to get clear with his or her self, or even to make his peace with heaven?

Not a chance. When all is said and done, we are simply spreading disinformation, fear and impotence. What is the point of giving a condemned man daily reports on the preparations for his execution? Since we are continuing to portay politicians as responsible beings (and in our leader articles to appeal to their sense of responsibility and their ability to act freely), a totally false but traditional view of them, in the present situation the only conclusion that anyone can draw is that they are either idiots or criminals. Or perhaps it is really true to say that the final purpose of history is the extinction of human civilisation, and these men are merely that purpose's puppets.

Other newspapers, as well as the radio and the television, are trying to spread a feeling of confidence and hope. The panic reactions and desperate demonstrations of the past few days show, however, that the public has begun to give up hope. The escalation of the confict between the two superpowers seems unstoppable; for days now there has been no sign of any slowing down in the headlong rush to the abyss. At the end of that road is universal, global destruction. What hope is there in that scenario?

In the final analysis, we journalists are simply being asked to do the impossible, because the course of the crisis has obviously got out of the politicians' control. Everything is running in accordance with long-prepared options, automatically. Such a reality is outside our experience, however. The press failed, when the opportunity was there, to intervene in the preparation and development of these options and to make them the subject of public debate. We never investigated the basis of this security policy, or explored its contradictions and dead ends.

We allowed ourselves to fall in with the politicians' and the generals' way of seeing things. Deterrence, defence, protection, superiority, parity, victory, defeat – concepts that have become meaningless in the era of nuclear weapons – were all ideas that we clarified and interpreted until they seemed to make sense, even though they bore no relation to nuclear reality. As Nietzsche once complained, we 'let time go by without considering the nature of humanity'.

We failed, but always continued to behave as if we knew better. Now all we journalists can do, just like everyone else, is to gaze at the doomsday machine in motion, like rabbits facing a snake.

Why do I stay at my desk? Why do I keep putting together news, when all it really says is that life on earth will soon no longer exist? Why am I so dedicated to communicating as true as possible a picture of the coming apocalypse? My work has become meaningless. Its only purpose is to stop me from facing my own fundamental existential questions. To prepare oneself for the inevitable and to accept it for a reality is probably the only chance left of keeping some human dignity.

Are we really the last link in this chain of thousands of generations? The thought is so fantastic and yet so hideous that I don't dare think it through. At the moment I am in the same situation as the monkey in Kafka's *Report to an Academy*: my goal is not freedom, but just a way out.

2nd August, midnight

Since eight this evening, hourly repeated demands for the last six years' conscripts to report to their posts immediately. The reservists are being called up, so the crisis point must have arrived. Tomorrow the emergency laws come into force. Parliament is being sent home, except for a small remnant for appearance's sake. Rationing, restrictions, organisational measures, as if we were facing a long war on some far frontier. This whole scenario is out of the 1950s; it has had no relevance to nuclear reality since then. The product of some desk-bound bureaucrats which has outlived its time – and theirs – by forty years. But I am convinced that 'the responsible authorities' see some meaning in it and actually believe in the necessity of these measures. One of the reasons why the self-deception is so grotesque. Doctors and hospital staff have been told to report and have themselves registered in accordance with the Law for the Maintenance of Public Health.

The Federal Minister of the Interior has said that the Federal Government feels itself forced, along with its allies, to take these preventive measures, because preparations for war are going ahead at full speed in the East. These measures, the minister claims, will make it immediately clear to the enemy that he will encounter determined resistance from the West if he does not halt the escalation now. The enemy will thus be seen to be taking an incalculable risk.

And what about our risk? We are threatening the enemy with our own suicide. Extraordinarily effective! In any case, the Soviets are not running anywhere near as great a risk as we are. They and the Americans will be able to watch on television screens as Germany is turned into a smoking nuclear wasteland. Whatever happens, we will be first, and they will only suffer later. But we will have the comfort of having deterred them by our horrific example!

Andreas rang up. His civilian auxiliary service time had been due to run out the day after tomorrow. But he won't come home. The disabled old people he has been working with would be absolutely alone and there would be no one to care for them. Most of the relatives are either uncontactable or are refusing to take in grandpa or grandma. His replacement has not arrived yet, three of the doctors have been called up, another doctor and three orderlies disappeared yesterday. He said he had to stay in Bielefeld whatever happened. But he was with us in his thoughts.

He said that things were quite all right up there, because the crippled old people, with their inner tranquillity and acceptance,

54

were really uplifting; most of them even found the strength to be fun, and they were very loyal. Frau Pauli, a resolute lady who constantly talked to herself – mostly complaints – was announcing once every hour, to general agreement, that she intended to go out there and sort things out, put an end to the insanity in the outside world.

Tomorrow Christine will be arriving with Ralf. She rang up from Lyons. Difficult to get anywhere in France too. Jammed roads, vacationers pouring back to their homes, and the roads leading to the German border filled with motorised army units. I am very glad that Christine is coming. On the other hand, though, I would rather they were still in relative safety in the South of France.

I feel helpless and passive. I wish I could fall asleep now and never wake up again. One day, maybe soon, the fulfilment of that particular wish may count as the greatest mercy. We shall have to arrange that for ourselves, each of us. It is a curious notion that millions of human beings will become, to all intents, one person: the same fears, the same hopes, the same desires. And more or less the same end.

3rd August, afternoon

The Soviets are landing troops and heavy material on the Kuril Islands. Apparently this is their 'unshakeable response' to the Japanese mobilisation. Everyone claims only to be responding. Everyone is simply taking defensive measures, everyone is feeling they are being threatened, and everyone claims that what they really want is peace. Together they are working towards the final inferno. Nietzsche hoped that 'a great day would come when a nation, distinguished by wars and victories, by the highest development of military order and wisdom, will call out: 'We break our sword' . . . will make itself defenceless, where before it was the most capable of defending itself, simply because it has reached a certain height of sensibility – this is the way to real peace.' Utopia. Crucial and utopian.

Heavy air battles over the Sea of Ochotsk. China has moved seven million men to her northern border – as *extra* support!

55

Cuba has been as good as occupied, though the Cubans are still offering a bitter resistance in some towns and in the mountains. Mexico has left the Organisation of American States in protest against the US attitude.

The Federal Government, representatives of the Bundestag, of the political parties and the top government departments, are getting ready to move to a nuclear-proof bunker in the Eifel. This is just a precautionary measure, says the government spokesman. There was still hope that the other side would see reason.

Always expecting reason from the other side. Where is our own? Both sides are doing the same thing.

'Reason' within the framework of the deterrence system means weakness, for the other side could interpret it as surrender. The wiser side would climb down in this situation – but in the nuclear age this is not allowed. Every psychotic considers himself the personification of reason – and his brand of reason is being persecuted.

What kind of human beings are going down into that bomb-proof bunker now? A move that has been planned for a long time and practised over and over. Are they men who have feelings, who love other human beings, who need affection themselves? These top politicians, parliamentarians and officials have now left behind their wives and children, without knowing whether they will ever see them again. A shining example, the first to make that sacrifice? To me it seems to be much more the soulless execution of a plan, a measure agreed decades ago. The real victims are the people who will be living in those bunkers. And we shall be theirs. Have they seen the fear in the eyes of their wives and children? Have they taken notice of it? If they were really convinced that there was still hope, they would not be hiding in their bunker. Voyeurs of their own destruction, and that of their families.

How will this 'example' affect those who have no bunkers or shelters?

A sarcastic article in the paper. In 1945, a last handful of our rulers also sat in a bunker and hoped for better times. In vain.

Christine and Ralf have arrived. The joy of seeing each other again was already overshadowed by a sense of impending loss.

Queues outside the food stores, and also outside other shops. Everyone aiming to make it through the catastrophe. Perhaps the act of purchasing and the sight of those hoarded goods at home has a calming effect. In past times of crisis, to have sufficient provisions was considered to be half the technique of survival.

Human beings can only act according to learned notions and experiences. Nuclear reality is beyond any imagination, let alone tradition. All it causes is a diffuse anxiety; it makes even instinctual reactions obsolete. To flee is pointless, as is self-protection or retaliation. We can do nothing for our children. Any readiness to save others by sacrificing ourselves can never be translated into action. We cannot even comfort ourselves. All we can do is resign, give up hope. On the one hand, the threat is an abstract one at the moment, something we learn about through reading, or hearing the news, reports, documentaries. We cannot see the danger, or hear it. It is there, always there, but it could, of course, just disappear again. The thought of war and the fear of war bring atavistic ideas up out of the unconscious, these traditional, learned attitudes. One such is the hoarding of food, and another is building a bunker or burrow, like my neighbour Thönnessen has done in his garden. Instinct and experience alike demand that we see things through, survive for as long as possible, every extra second or hour, put off the evil moment of extinction for every day we can.

The total quality and the horrifying predictability of nuclear war, however, demands the opposite of us; a way of behaviour that goes totally against instinct and experience and actually has us do everything we can to make the end come as quickly as possible, and with as little pain – including terrifying, intolerable experiences – as we can manage.

But since counter-instinctual behaviour such as this is not possible, a sort of normality seems to have infected everyone at this stage in the crisis. Everyone is trying, as best they can, to organise their own survival. The media are offering good suggestions, experts are appearing and giving tips, and pamphlets are being distributed to the public. 'How do I protect myself from explosions and heat? –' – 'How do I protect myself from radiation?' – 'How do I decontaminate myself and my family?' – 'What do I need for a good home medicine chest?' – 'First aid made easy' – 'How do I behave if there is panic?'

This is, of course, all quite futile, but it makes the catastrophe conceivable, reduces it to the kind of proportions that we can accept. The coming nuclear war may be ten, a hundred times worse than the Second World War – at least so long as we keep naming figures like that, we can encompass it. And this allows a chance of survival, no matter how tiny it may be. And above all, it allows us to go beyond survival and to think of a future world. Whether this world will be worth living in is something that the instructions manuals don't consider.

This is how discipline is maintained. The masses will not rise up and take their fate out of the hands of the politicians. They will not prevent the catastrophe, because they can keep hoping to the last. They are victims of their own limited psychology and their own limited imaginations.

I am deeply depressed. Despairing. All this looks like a clever ruse on the part of the politicians. But it is not. The politicians themselves have fallen victim to the same psychological, emotional and intellectual limitations. The nuclear reality is beyond their imaginative capacity too. It is the only explanation of why things have been allowed to get this far. They did not know what they were doing. And they still don't. Their survival in their bunker will force them to realise it. That will be a punishment that I wouldn't wish on anyone, even them.

The train was empty today. Usually travellers have to stand as far as Hoechst, often until Eddernheim. The endless appeals by the government, the employers and the trade unions for people to go to work – the Chancellor: 'It is the best contribution to peace that anyone can make' – seem to be having little effect.

The train moved towards the setting sun, which cast golden stripes across the river Main. The vineyards near Hofheim heavy and ripe. It would have been a great vintage. Now nothing but rain. The Taunus is like a blue ribbon. Yellow and green fields, factories, housing estates, one after the other. A landscape that has been over-settled, maybe ruined, but at least alive.

Will these fields soon be black, the villages razed or empty, the Taunus incinerated? It is impossible to imagine it.

The Galaxy transport aircraft and the Starlifters were hanging in the grey bell of mist above the Rhine-Main airport like fat queen bees.

3rd August, midnight

Friends came to see us in the evening. Depressive and oppressive atmosphere. What was going to happen next? Everyone worried at that question, and no one had an answer. That 'Bloody Sunday' was perhaps still too fresh in our memories, like a nightmare that will not go away. We can't even help each other. Everyone knows that. Ashen faces. The worst thing is that fear leads to alienation between human beings. Everyone lives in his own glass case, incapable of communication. Chain-smoking, clutching our wine glasses. We are all looking for something to hold onto. Long silences. Embarrassment. The sound of cutlery.

I was unable to bring myself out of my depressed mood. We infected each other. Verena Voss came close to crying.

When it had become intolerable, Tina finally said that we were not at a funeral, and asked Hans von Raitzen to say something. Hans finished chewing his roast beef first. He loves being asked his opinion. He is the big cultural cheese in Wiesbaden. A painter with the build and features of a Rasputin, but also a very sensitive aesthete. His broad face has settled into fine, wry folds.

The present nuclear madness, he said at last, was attributable to the fact that modern human beings had destroyed aesthetic values. Their powers of judgement had suffered accordingly, as Kant realised a long time ago. For a long time, in fact, a distriction of our cultural values had been clearly discernible. Modern man had cut his traditional roots, the autonomy of the individual personality was a thing of the past, the notion of the *kalokagatos*, the morally wise and good human being, the ideal of beauty, was no longer needed.

All we need to do is compare the cultural foundation

underpinning a man like Bismarck, compared with the present Federal Chancellor, or compare Woodrow Wilson – whom he by no means valued particularly – with the present American president. There were worlds between them! The loss of aesthetic ideas and the destruction of culture, however, led directly to the dissolution of guiding values and of moral restraints. The world of the technical and the functional had taken over, and the actors on the political stage were simply its guardians.

To solve conflicts with nuclear weapons was currently the most functional method. Any ethical questions regarding the consequences of such an action were dismissed as old-fashioned moralising. The hideous excesses of modern architecture, with its complete lack of humanity, practically demanded mankind's elimination. For Hans, at any rate, the present situation came as no surprise.

Tina had been right. Raitzen's words, thought-provoking as ever, eased the mood. There were even touches of hilarity afterwards.

Verena intends to close down the further education college, now that there are just she and a few others there. Only a few old folk were still coming to classes. She has plans to go and stay with her parents at Langenhagen.

Dieter Karasch made his disagreement known with such energy that he came close to losing his glasses. He thought that the cities could actually be the safest places if the worse happened. He told this to people in his office at City Hall all the time. He could not imagine they would attack the cities. What possible interest could the Soviets have in a bloodbath such as that? The Americans would also spare centres of population. It was terrible enough to use tactical nuclear weapons on the battlefield. The danger was greater in the country than in the cities.

Sometimes, despite all the brave words, we realised that we were impotent dinner-table strategists. But what else was there to talk about? It was true that none of us would have wanted to change places with the people in the Eifel, the Hunsrück or the Swabian Alp – who had been waiting for the blow to fall for days now, for the nuclear inferno to descend on them. But if the Pershing and Cruise Missile bases there were attacked, it would certainly be all up for us too.

Hans von Raitzen says he feels like a gravestone that has fallen over; what an effort it takes to keep upright and carry on with daily activity. The collective threat that hangs over each of our individual existences still causes a kind of incredulous amazement.

We make arrangements to stay in close contact.

The total nature of nuclear weapons and the apparently inevitable spectre of the apocalypse has finally answered the ancient question: What is the purpose of history? The 'meaning' of history is nothing more than a purposeful, deterministic evolution towards self-destruction. Nietzsche's 'will to nothingness'. The myths of almost all peoples and civilisations deal in an eschatology that ends in the destruction of the world. Prophetic? Or simply predictable?

It is impossible to think of the moral associations connected with ideas such as 'self-destruction', 'extinction', 'extermination', 'holocaust', 'inferno', 'catastrophe', and 'apocalypse', or we end up with questions of guilt or failure of responsibility. Such questions only fudge our insights and with it the last freedom we can exercise: the freedom to dare to gaze into nothingness and to choose to continue living.

This forced, pre-determined course of events in the past few days is merely part of the technical preparation for the end of history and human civilisation. It also makes it clear – too late, admittedly – that the possibility of an alternative to this, even on a theoretical level, has never existed. Things could have been no different under other conditions or political constellations or other leaders. This had to happen. What is occurring now might have been delayed – through chance – but not prevented. The course of history is above questions of responsibility, failure, guilt. Human free will is conditioned by teleological and especially eschatological necessities.

For centuries we have been deceived by the ability of our reason to indulge in utopian or alternative thinking, to have intellectual freedom. This ability, however, brought the deceptive notion that man was in control of his own history, which meant that mistakes in evolution could be corrected.

The horrifying truths contained in myths and eschatological

61

systems. Whether they propose a twilight of the gods, the obscuring of the sun as the source of life, or icy cold, or collapse of the sky, the stars' falling, or the earth sinking into the sea – history always ends in a catastrophe, one facilitated by the way civilisations develop. The meaning is in the end, and no more.

If the myth-tellers had been able to take a glance into the Twentieth century, they would have put their apocalypse in the form of exploding hydrogen bombs.

I remember a radio report at the end of the Fifties or the beginning of the Sixties about a conference at the Vatican, during the course of which several theologians referred to the prophetic power of the Revelation of St John and raised the question of whether God might not be using a few politicians and military men as instruments to prepare the end of the world through nuclear weapons. The horrified reporter spoke of an 'insane argument'. He refused, like most of those present, to accept this interpretation. But in St John's 'apocalypse' we can actually read: '. . . and there came hail and fire mingled with blood, and this was hurled upon the earth; and a third of the earth was burnt . . . A third of the sea was turned to blood, a third of the living creatures in it died . . . men in great numbers died because of the water because it had been poisoned . . . others were tormented for months, with torment like a scorpion's sting . . . and men will seek death; they will long to die, but death will elude them . . . Woe, woe to those who live upon the earth.'

In comparison, scientists' and physicians' accounts of the nuclear inferno seem on the dry side.

Our assumption that the Apocalypse was somehow an expiation of our guilt has always displaced the question onto the moral level. Thus the idea of a merciful and benevolent God remained possible, an Almighty who can eliminate humanity physically, but save our souls and deliver them to a better world. Any insights into the merciless determinism of the natural process involved were distorted by these ideas.

Dark thoughts. But the acceptance of an omnipotent fate in the form of natural evolution contains some comfort. It does nothing to alleviate the fear, but it lessens the despair for people.

According to tradition, the Apócalypse was written by John, a man, and a morbid lust for destruction is clearly communicated, driven home by powerful language. There is a correspondingly lusty suppression of the female: 'Yet I have this against you: You tolerate that Jezebel, the woman who claims to be a prophetess, who by her teaching lures my servants into fornication and by eating food sacrificed to idols. I have given her time to repent , but she refuses to repent of her fornication.'

What fear of the female, the mother, the life principle! All these are founded in Judaeo-Christian civilisation, which attempted to control history and evolved a uniquely repressive moral code. It is no accident that wars broke out periodically, regularly.

Because of cultural developments and the social consequences of suppressed human drives, Freud considered that wars would be 'unavoidable' for the foreseeable future, but put his hopes in the 'gentle but in the long term inexorable voice of reason.'

Freud could have avoided this mistake; but then he also must have feared looking into nothingness. His pupil, K.R. Eissler, obviously did not share this fear: 'If, however, wars in our culture are not simply the result of powerful aggressive feelings, but are based on traditions buried deep in the collective morality, protected from criticism by the charisma of holiness, then when we fight for a lasting peace we are backing a lost cause. Instead we should recognise the inevitability of war in our times.'

Maleness – patriarchy – suppression of women – repressive morality – aggression – aggressive culture – repressive societies – hostility to desire and life – wars – apocalypse. The evangelist: 'She is fallen . . . and has become a dwelling for demons and a haunt for every unclean spirit, for every foul and loathsome bird . . . Come, I will show you the judgment over the great whore who sits on many waters . . . and all nations have drunk deep of the fierce wine of her fornication.'

For five hundred years, until the early Eighteenth century, any husband could denounce a wife who displeased him as a witch – and any horny monk could do the same for a woman who pleased him. She would end up at the stake. Millions of women were burnt, in many towns and villages only two or

63

three would be left. Alongside the woman as whore was the pure, spotless virgin.

The suppression of women in the Judaeo-Christian tradition begins, of course, right with the myth of creation. In contrast to most other creation myths, the making of the world is not seen as a birth from a primeval mother, but in a sense as a product of intelligence, a 'birth in the head' or the construction of a man. The rational principle, which became the basis of man's actions from now on, gained its victory over the devalued principle of the organic-animal. So the first human being is a man, and from his rib woman is 'born.' Grotesque.

Isn't the thought of salvation and the promise of paradise more like the infantile desire for a return to the womb? To be a child again, to have total satisfaction, be without guilt, not to have to face up to life, to enjoy the kindly demi-existence that comes before birth?

Since this desire is incapable of fulfilment, there is the substitute satisfaction of death. Back to Mother Earth as a corpse. Perhaps the tragedy of the male is that he has to separate himself by force from the all-powerful, loving mother because otherwise she will 'devour' his manhood. Man asserting his identity by rejecting the female?

4th August, mid-day

A well-prepared, nationwide blow delivered against the Left. Arrests of leading members of the German Communist Party, other communists and also leaders of the civil rights organisations. The Humanistic Union, the Gustav-Heinemann Initiative, Committee for Basic Rights, Action Expiation, Live without Armaments, and even Pax Christi have been declared organisations hostile to the state from this morning.

This catalogue of banned organisations was obviously taken from the last Report for the Protection of the Constitution put together by the Minister of the Interior, heftily extended. The emergency laws have made it possible. Along with restrictions on organisations, a ban on 'left-wing radical newspapers, magazines and publications'. Most of their publishers and editors have been arrested. Obviously an act of 'self-purification' for the country so far as many conservatives are concerned. For them the emergency has its good side.

I was dragged out of bed by the doorbell this morning, interrogated by three gentlemen from the Office for the Protection of the Constitution. They searched my study thoroughly. Seized essays and articles 'for their records'. The only thing they failed to find was my diary.

Discreet, thorough types, politely distant, always looking straight ahead. As if in blinkers?

For my part, I am curious and interested in these men and their job: 'Why do you do this?' Answer from the man with the scrubbed, clean-shaven face: 'Because we have been given appropriate instructions.'

'And that's it as far as you're concerned?'

'Amazed: 'Yes, of course.'

Do you let your own thoughts be part of the work you have been told to carry out?'

'I have to put them to one side, they are nothing to do with this.'

'Could you imagine that you are aiding a policy that is leading us into catastrophe.'

'That's not my problem.'

'What is the problem so far as you are concerned?'

'The fact that you are suspected of indulging in activities that could weaken the defensive capability of the state! And I have to investigate that.'

'But what if it is just those activities of the state that threaten us – and you and your family – whereas I, and the others you are proceeding against, are trying to avert that threat?'

As before, friendly, almost as if humouring me: 'I can't think about that. We are doing our duty.'

'Can you imagine doing the wrong duty, letting yourself be misused?'

'So long as that duty is based on the law: No.'

'And if your convictions, perhaps even your conscience, told you that "legality" in this situation was wrong or foolish, something that had to be stopped by resistance or disobedience?'

Still working away at his search, sort of in passing: 'Oh, you

65

must realise that the state has to be sure that its officials put their own opinions to one side.'

'Are you frightened?'

'Perhaps. But not while I'm on duty.'

As they were packing my essay *The War Memoirs* into their bag, I showed them a passage in it which contained a serious pun: 'War memoirs are all very well, but unfortunately in Germany, soldiers seem to have no memories.'

'Good point,' said the smooth-shaven agent amicably. The three gentlemen left, obviously amused.

The Chancellor is appealing to the people to support the recently-introduced defence measures and to 'give their innermost assent'. Germans had never before in history defended a more just cause. It was a worthwhile thing to be defending our christian-western civilisation. Defence was always just. Unless a nation was prepared to defend itself, it would be destroyed, or at least lose its identity and dignity, be cut off from its roots. Freedom was worth any sacrifice. The President of the USA had just told him on the telephone that the United States stood ready to defend its allies with all its power.

The Chancellor actually said 'any sacrifice'. The sacrifices demanded by total nuclear war are entire people. And if there are no people, there is no freedom. Lord forgive them, for they know not what they do. But we are howling out our despair at an empty heaven.

Of course, the generals and the Americans will ensure that the Red Army doesn't manage to occupy and hold a square metre of Western territory. Tactical nuclear weapons will take care of that. Defence is possible, but at what a price, with what sacrifices! *Any* sacrifice. Total weapons demand total sacrifice, which means our freedom too.

The Americans (and the Soviets) will defend themselves to the last German. 60 million dead or maimed Germans are a reasonable price to pay for America's or Russia's 'freedom'. The defence of Germany will be really total.

At the end, the Chancellor advises everyone to keep their radios and televisions switched on at all times.

Einstein: 'The freeing of the atom has changed everything –

except the way human beings think.' The public statements of our politicians and spiritual leaders during the past few years provide depressing proof of this. In an interview with *Der Spiegel* some years ago, Cardinal Josef Ratzinger, for instance, called the French and British nuclear missiles 'weapons for defence'. The kind of thoughtless statement that leads automatically to a fatally wrong-headed ethical conclusion: it is true that defensive weapons are ethically legitimate, but nuclear weapons can never be used for defence or for protection – the physical warding-off of an aggressor – only for attack, or revenge, or deterrence by terror. Deterrence, however, involves the threat of either revenge or attack. Neither of these are ethically justifiable – at least by Christian standards. Therefore nuclear weapons are not ethically justifiable under any circumstance, independently of political usefulness or – paradoxically – the ethical aim of preventing war through their possession.

Do German officers recognise binding ethical principles? Empirical reason? Conscience? How can officers, who are experts, let the politicians burden them with the label 'defensive' without a thought? An argument we often hear quoted: the politicians create the framework, we just make it work. That is our job.

Justification or excuse? Cowardice? A lack of basic civil courage?

Defence is only possible if the Soviets keep to the scenario that NATO has created: the Russians attack according to plan with the conscious aim of conquering Europe and helping communism to global victory. Initially the fight is with conventional weapons. The Warsaw Pact is poised for victory, since NATO is hopelessly inferior in this area. NATO uses nuclear weapons 'selectively', 'limitedly', 'in planned escalation'. The Soviets are then supposed to see the risk and pull back. The USA threatens use of strategic weapons. The Soviets see the risk and withdraw – they had been, of course, too stupid to foresee this.

Scenario complete.

Basic questions: what if the Soviets attack, not with premeditated conquest in mind but because of fear, misconceptions, false assumptions, mistakes, blunders? What if they use nuclear weapons straightaway and don't wait for NATO to do it? What if, after the 'selective' use of tactical nuclear weapons by NATO they retaliate on a massive scale and turn Germany, Europe, into a nuclear wasteland? What if they see a pre-emptive strike as the lesser risk?

What if it should prove true that it always takes two to wage war?

And in order to sustain the illusion of 'defence', German officers – just like German politicians – have to base everything on what are no more than assumptions. The biggest assumption is: the Soviets will behave exactly the way we expect them to. Absolutely can't behave any other way. Wishful thinking. A circular argument. And if the Soviets don't behave according to these assumptions, then there will, as far as I can see, be no defence policy left. And therefore no reason for the existence of a conventional army.

Do German officers refuse to oppose this concept of 'defence' so that their own position isn't brought into question? An ethical failure? Suppression of their own superior understanding? Denial of conscience?

A grotesque contradiction – one of countless others. Politically we project onto the Soviets a 'worse case' situation, which means we assume their readiness to conquer, threaten, to blackmail us and force their will on us, and to generally exercise all their possible options at once. We are arming to face this 'worst case'. Militarily, however, we have to depend on the fact that the Russians, if war comes, will not even exercise a fraction of their options: no attacks on nuclear reactors, not using even five percent of their tactical nuclear weapons against the Federal Republic – and that alone would be thirty times the total of bombs and shells used in the Second World War – and holding off from attacking the military targets that threaten them. Otherwise they will bomb us out of existence.

When in the history of warfare have enemies held off from using the most effective weapons in their possession? Shouldn't a responsible policy proceed from the most likely scenario, and not from the most unlikely?

The way John Doe imagines defence policy is just the way it

is, as Kurt Tucholsky said. I despair of this permanent blindness, which seems to go on from age to age. Determinism? Not an ethical problem: they believe in the way their reality is, so as not to have to see the actual situation, which is indefensible.

Is it any comfort that East German officers probably think the same way? That they too make a meaningless distinction between tactical and strategic nuclear weapons? That they too – 'in good faith' – will stand up for the security interests of another nation at the cost of their own people – and maybe in the very near future will carry out their orders. For national suicide.

Carl von Clausewitz: 'To stir an army into action when there is no opportunity for the realisation of political goals by military means, is a crime.'

But to stir up a nation? There is not the slightest chance of attaining a political goal by the military means available. Have we been singled out so that our annihilation will serve as an example, so that the surviving nations will learn from this 'greatest of humanity's tragedies' to curb their destructive impulses and make them subject to the rule of reason?

4th August, evening

Mobilisation is proceeding with a kind of moronic perfection. All the scenarios practised and perfected in countless manoeuvres are being put into operation. It would be easy to believe that the politicians are acting out of a bizarre kind of defiance. A powerful machine is being activated, a machine that impresses itself – if no one else – and which has given itself the illusion of defensive capability, because the tactical nuclear weapons and the enemy's attitude have been 'forgotten'.

This country's most peaceful – or at least peaceloving – generation in history is being called up. Called to arms. A million reservists are 'hurrying to the colours'. The fatherland calls. This generation – knowing and yet caring, resigned and yet creative, patient and impatient, cursing and protesting, waiting its chance, tough and yet tender – has now been summoned to participate in the greatest mess that humanity has ever faced, but mainly, if the truth were told, to let it wash over them. They will have no chance to fight. They will never write letters home from the front. They will be victims. But they don't know it. They are already victims, because they believe in 'defence' and thus in their task of protecting their homeland and freedom. The deluded are always victims.

I think of the colonel who at the end of the Seventies was transferred from Bonn to a staff job in Brussels, and who took a year to come to the realisation that 'Five times I have taken part in a war game. The Federal Republic was defended five times, and it was destroyed five times.' Another Bundeswehr officer: 'The message is "no surrender", even at the price of our own annihilation'.

Since the NATO decision that allowed the stationing of Pershings and Cruise Missiles, Europe has taken the final steps that have made it the hostage of the two superpowers. Until then, what would the Soviet Union's thousands of missiles been able to do to us? Just annihilate us. What could they have done with 300 SS-20s? Just annihilate us. Without the SS-20s? Also annihilate us. What extra military possibilities did the Soviets actually gain from their SS-20 armaments? None. Just a capacity to annihilate us ten, twenty or thirty times instead of just once. Would that have done them any good? No. Would they have felt free to turn Europe into a nuclear inferno? No. Such an inferno would have swept away the political system in the Soviet Union. We would have been able to assume that the Soviets would hold back from that degree of cold-blooded, planned barbarism. Would they have been able to blackmail us with the SS-20? No! Not against our wills. We would have refused to give in to the threat of short-range weapons, which are just as lethal for us as the SS-20s. Would the SS-20s have to have a deterrent effect on us? No, because overkill potential is not a deterrent. We can only die once.

Did we have to arm to meet that 'threat'? No. Was it politically necessary? It was a disaster. Have the new weapons made us more secure? They have pushed us Europeans close to the abyss.

The ABC of defence policy. A child could understand it.

Do the Pershings and Cruise Missiles have a deterrent effect on the Soviets? They push them deeper into the sense of terror that western policymakers have been encouraging for years now. But this sense of terror will only provoke the Soviets to a terrifying response. The existence of the Pershings has robbed them of their last scruples about attacking Europe and Germany. Their nuclear armaments have suddenly been granted a kind of retroactive justification – and a function. We are now Soviet hostages. Our fate is totally dependent on whatever fourteen elderly men in the Kremlin decide to do during the next few hours or days. Our fate is no longer dependent on the Federal Government, or the Bundeswehr, or NATO.

We are also, however, hostage of the USA. The 'surgical strokes' that they will inflict on the Soviet élite with the Pershings will be at our cost too. 'We have to be in a position to "decapitate" the Soviet Union, in order to make inoperative the entire political and military power structure of the Soviet Union and its allies.' The death sentence on the Federal Republic of Germany is already there for all to read in the American *Fiscal Year 1984–1988 Defense Guidance*.

Colin S. Grey expressed it very clearly some years ago: 'The US should be planning to win a war against the Soviet Union, and at a cost that will permit an American recovery. Washington should establish war aims that ultimately include the destruction of Soviet political power and the creation of a postwar world order that corresponds to Western values.'

Those fools in their bunker in the Eifel believe that the Soviet ruling élite will allow itself to be 'decapitated' – with German help. Us or them. Which means, actually, us.

The paper has started a campaign encouraging our readers to express their feelings about the present situation and to let the government know their deep unease and their fear regarding the uncompromising policy of confrontation being pursued by our ally, the USA, as well as the Soviets. The Federal Government needs to be clear that we cannot 'survive' a war, even a conventional one.

Will the postal service deliver the forms that we supply with the paper? Some doubts about that.

The masses have become superfluous to requirements so far as

71

waging a war is concerned. 'Imagine they had a war and nobody went.' No one needs to 'go' anywhere for this war, for the few hours or days it lasts. The people are no longer needed. They just get in the way.

The anxious mood at work continues. A few are pretending they can take it, falling back on black humour, while others are apathetic and still others' nerves are completely shot. I am one of the last group.

Defence policy and the East-West conflict can be classified as variations on a theme of persecution, paranoia or psychosis. It is always the other's fault. He is the one who has made all the preparations, is just lying in wait for the right moment to strike, when I lay myself open. He is trying to tempt me with gestures of peace, offers of disarmament and co-operation. Clever plans, worked out long in advance. Very skilful. My enemy is powerful, can afford to wait, is cunning and icy cold. Dirty tricks, but I see through them immediately. Wants to get me helpless and then have his way with me. But I won't play that game. I shall defend myself. The enemy will realise just what I'm capable of, whatever the cost. Then we'll see who's really got what it takes when the trouble starts . . .

Alfred Adler: *Psychosis is a very male disease*.
Goethe: *War is in truth a disease*.

4th August, midnight

Neighbour Thönnessen's example has really started a trend. Everyone in Taunusrodt is digging away frantically in their gardens, creating 'shelters' according to the instructions issued by the German Self-Protection Society. One has been infecting the other. The rest are anxious because they don't have gardens.

The brochure says: 'The heat storm created by a nuclear explosion can affect places kilometres away, depending on the strength of the explosion, and can easily set alight to combustible material such as paper, wood, varnish, curtains. The air pressure can turn window panes into shrapnel that can cause severe injuries.' Wiesbaden is the other side of the plateau. A marvellous description: 'Self-protection'. We'll make our war,

72

and you have to protect yourself. Just mind where you choose to be when the bomb drops.

Farmer Brand at the end of the village is converting his old cesspool into a 'shelter'. Self-protection.

A walk with Tina. In the rays of the setting sun, the fishponds looked as if they had been filled with liquid bronze. The cool of the evening did us good. Everywhere there was the scent of fullness, ripeness. The birds were singing in the hedgerows. The land is thirsty for rain. The twilight blanketed the sparse woods, the scraggy pine trees and beeches, the untidy little glades, the feeble-looking plantations of young trees. The landscape seemed already to have an air of the past about it. Once upon a time . . .

But then there is Tina, walking close beside me. Andreas, who doesn't want to leave his old people. Christine.

'There is so much that is terrible in mankind – the earth has been a madhouse for too long.' Reading Nietzsche again. That sick, suffering visionary exercises an almost masochistic fascination over me. He spent a lifetime experiencing the conditions that created the 'sick animal', man, and he finally died of that experience. 120 years later, we are also dying of it.

'In some distant corner of a universe teeming with glittering systems of suns, there was once a brain with which some clever creatures discovered the ability to perceive. It was the proudest and most deceptive moment in "world history". But it was only a moment. After nature had taken a few more breaths, the brain atrophied, and the clever creatures had to die. Anyone could write a fable along those lines, and still it would not suffice to show how pathetic, how shadowy, how indifferent, how purposelessness and fickle is the human intellect when we set it against the scale of nature. There have been eternities when it did not exist, and when it has gone, it will be as if it never was.'

How horribly true. If we think of the earth's history as a day, the species mankind has existed for three seconds, and *homo sapiens* with his intellect only for fractions of a second. Has existed. Intellect and consciousness came and disappeared like an explosion. Is that what the hundreds of millions of years of preparation were for?

In order to create a sense of liberation from the suffering

73

caused by an increasingly irrational and sterile way of life, mankind made for himself the notion of 'salvation', sacred and profane. Recently there has been a transition from longing for a better world and dreams of paradise to more concrete political and social fantasies. But the notion of 'salvation' will only really die when the first nuclear bombs fall and unleash the worldwide holocaust. Our fantasies were first threatened when nuclear weapons became a reality and we began to threaten each other with their use. This 'trying out period' was the twilight of christian-western civilisation, the falling away from God. The threat and the implied readiness to cause the destruction of the world amounted in itself to a severing of all connection with ethical or humane values. Those in power in the churches have not grasped that.

At the same time, Marxism has also failed to keep pace with history. It supposed the establishment of a society free of all repression, in which mankind as a social being would be able to behave according to his nature, which means rationally and well, and in which peace would be secured as a historical necessity. In fact, the unfolding of productive forces in socialist societies has brought with it the unfolding of total armament as a way of life. Marx and Engels would spin in their graves if they could see how the USSR, the first workers' and peasants' state, is prepared to annihilate the workers and peasants of other nations at the push of a button.

Once we have a situation where nuclear weapons could end human history at any moment – never mind whether because of some devilish scheme, or because of a mistake, or some psychotic or historical compulsion – then we can say goodbye to any thesis that supposes the aim of human history to be the inevitable establishment of some society free of repression and suffering, in which all will give according to their abilities and receive according to their needs.

The simple fact of the nuclear threat totally denies the most central tenets of Marxism. Its guardians have never recognised that. Or they have recognised it and ignored it.

And enlightened humanism? Empirical reasoning and ethics do not determine human behaviour. Freud: *There is no such thing as an autonomous will as a constant, historically and*

74

socially formative factor. Despite our perceptions, our ability to reason. Kant: *Peace is the masterpiece of reason.* But other determining factors are stronger.

And so Christians, Marxists and humanists are all busily working together to prove that their beliefs and convictions are totally mistaken.

We can, indeed perhaps we must, interpret European history thus: as a history of wars, punctuated by truces. And truces are nothing but times for rearming. 'Our task is not to keep the peace but to create it, for we have no peace. We live in a situation of permanent armed alert, a truce that cannot hold for ever.' Bertha von Suttner in 1896!

A truce from 1871 to 1914. War. Truce from 1918 to 1939. War. A truce from 1945 to 1998? Eissler is right in believing that 'war plays a larger role in the history of the West than in that of other civilisations.' That is hardly surprising. Helmut von Moltke: 'War is a part of God's natural world order.' Ludendorff: 'War is a nation's fountain of youth.'

Nothing new under the sun. Except for the new weapons. And new weapons have always been too much for generals to handle.

5th August, mid-day

Panic has broken out among the population close to the nuclear reactors. Almost the entire populations of Southern Hessen and Southern Baden are literally fleeing from the reactor at Biblis, most of them to the south and the west. A resurgence of hysteria. The threat of war is constant and relentless, and its permanence has helped people to remember what they once learned. What they learned: a direct hit by a missile on a 'hot' reactor will turn an area of a thousand square kilometres around into a charnel house. The reactor is like having a car packed with explosives at your front door. It is as if you can hear the timer ticking away. The public believes that war will be total. The government's placebos have been totally ineffective. Germany has become like a rabbit's hutch that has been broken into by a fox. Whichever way the rabbit jumps, the lethal danger is still there, and there is no escape.

This morning, hundreds of cars with Wiesbaden number plates

turned up suddenly in Taunusrodt. There were traffic jams in the middle of the village. Collisions. Local farmers were driving their tractors down the main street. Police and Border Protection troops managed to turn back the tide of vehicles. Curses and some resistance, scuffles, and finally warning shots.

Road blocks have appeared around Wiesbaden on all the exit roads. Anyone trying to leave the city is thoroughly inspected.

My attempt to get to Frankfurt by car via Fischbach and Königstein failed.

The news on the radio: The terrified public is being told that it is afraid. The government continues to try to establish calm by order.

Even people in Taunusrodt are aware that if the reactor in Biblis is destroyed, they will slowly go too. Given a light southerly wind, in something like two hours. But where can anyone go? The same danger everywhere, because those nuclear reactors are everywhere.

People are beginning to turn their sense of total impotence and helplessness against themselves and indulge in a kind of self-contempt. Arsehole, useless person, you can't do anything, not even clear off . . . We're all turning ourselves into frightened little rabbits. We can't even make ourselves useful. All we can do to 'help' is keep quiet, not rock the boat. Debilitating.

I arrive at a serious decision: before I turn into a miserable melancholic or go crazy, I shall sit back, as if I were in a front seat at the theatre, and try to be a spectator of all this. At least I shall be able to keep my humanity.

5th August, afternoon

The population of the border areas has also started to flee. They say that there is a mass evacuation in progress in the area south of Fulda. Troops moving forward towards the border are being held up by the masses of refugees. No more detailed information.

The villages are, after all, only two kilotons' worth of nuclear explosives apart. 'Collateral damage', the kind of 'marginal' destruction that no one wants but is unfortunately unavoidable.

Freedom has its price. I am forced to think of the film *Harttenbach* and of the American officer in the film who explained what 'defence' actually means: 'When the bomb went off over "ground zero", it would mean Harttenbach would be blown away. Gone, nothing, just a pile of dust about thirty centimetres high.' Many people didn't want to see that film, they thought like the mayor: 'Even if I have set a day for slaughtering my pig, I don't keep going into the animal to show it the knife, do I?' Now they can see the sword of Damocles hanging over them and realise that they are the sacrificial animal. They might have seen it a lot earlier if they had bothered to look up from their troughs. The sword has been hanging there for a long time now – as it has been over us all.

Eastern Hessen: Glorious countryside, full of old towns and beautiful half-timbered buildings. But also with hundreds of armaments depots, nuclear missile silos, military airfields, storage dumps, barracks, firing ranges. Practically a military camp for years now. The biggest powder-keg in the world. A prime target for any Soviet missile strategist. Every missile a direct hit, can't fail to connect . . .

Nevertheless, the population of East Hessen does have somewhere to run to – because anywhere is safer than home, even though that too is relative. In years past, the danger has been known, and that was that; now it has arrived and is immediate. That is the essential difference, though it has not been used politically.

In 1914, we went to war with cheering and flowers. In 1939 we accepted it in silence, but with our sleeves rolled up, ready to work. Now the nation is running for its life. However we Germans begin a war, it doesn't change a thing. We always end up the fall-guys.

Frankfurt and the other major cities have also been sealed off. Food and petrol rationing from today. Shops and banks are closed.

Is the population in the GDR and Czechoslovakia reacting in the same way? Probably exactly the same. Fear is international, and nuclear weapons have the same effect, whoever they hit.

More certain sightings of 'Moscow-inspired saboteurs' by the Minister of the Interior. He has promised strict counter-measures.

Has called on the populations of Eastern Hessen, East Lower Saxony and North-Eastern Bavaria not to allow themselves to be panicked. They have to realise that everything possible is being done for their protection. Troops and security forces are under strict orders to open fire if their preparations are 'hindered by persons or groups with clear intention of sabotage'. Roads to be used by commuters travelling to work have been clearly marked, the rest are closed to traffic. 'Normal life must continue.' Production must be maintained. If people are working, they will be too busy to have foolish thoughts.

I hear from the caretaker at our office building in Frankfurt that the paper will not be appearing tomorrow. Hardly anyone managed to get through to the office today.

5th August, midnight

Late this evening we were drinking a glass of wine as a nightcap. Suddenly a loud ringing at the door. To our amazement, a visit from Dr Petzold. Very embarrassed, forehead beaded with sweat, handkerchief in his hand. Profuse apologies. At first wouldn't even take a seat, but gratefully accepted a glass of wine immediately.

Petzold is a member of the Federal Parliament, owner of a chicken farm, a sawmill, chairman of the party faction in the district council, a member of the party's provincial committee, chairman of the district committee, involved in the sports club, the fire brigade, the farmers' league, the chamber of trade, the League for the Protection of German Forests, the parish council, the board of . . . all in all, on the committees of sixteen organisations – or is it eighteen? People call him the 'King of the Taunus'. Petzold used to hold court. His constituency surgeries were like audiences. Nothing happened without his say-so. A real boon to a journalist, because something was always going on in some club or society or other. My best enemy, and I his: to him I was always an agent of Moscow, supporter of Soviet plans for world domination, etc. A small, wiry figure, with round, steely-blue eyes, his toughness visible from the strong set of his chin, shoes with built-up heels, expensive aftershave, walks in the forest every morning, works out and swims at home. Always fit and on the ball. A phenomenon.

Now he looked as if he had lost any sense of orientation. Absent, constantly wiping his forehead with his handkerchief. No tie, which was a giveway.

His two sons were refusing to obey the call-up order. Were being 'egged on' by their mother. A disaster. The pair of them had cleared off and were in hiding. A disaster. What would his fellow-citizens say, or the party? He had brought up his sons to do their duty and to serve the community. Privileges also brought responsibilities. We had to constantly keep the good of the community in mind. That had always been the basis of his upbringing. Every community had the right to expect each individual to do his duty and fulfil his obligations. Otherwise no state would be viable. That his sons, of all people, had shirked their responsibility, was inexplicable. He would never get over it. He was totally bemused, he said, because this was the last thing he had expected.

My initial reaction: that the man was taking a complete liberty. Then we suddenly felt sorry for this pathetic human being. We understood why he had come to us: he wanted us to defend his sons. But we were also to help him save face. This man's world had fallen apart; the entire façade of his bourgeois existence no longer existed. In that context, his sons' behaviour appeared to him as a kind of betrayal. When a blind man on the street suddenly doubts where he is, he is lost. Petzold had never experienced doubt before.

And so I told him that all this had to be very depressing for him, I could well imagine the reaction of our fellow-citizens. However, I was in no position to help him. Since he had always been a whole-hearted supporter of the government's policy until now and was therefore part-responsible for the present situation, and since he was prepared even now to support the need for military 'defence', and to accept the costs and sacrifices involved, his sons' actions must seem to him as a dereliction of duty, even desertion in the face of the enemy.

Petzold nodded in a pained fashion with every sentence I said. Had he ever noticed any critical attitudes towards national security lately, even pacifistic ideas? It was quite common, after all, even for grown-up sons to hide a change of heart from a dominant father. Petzold denied the possibility vehemently: 'That's just it! It hit me like a bolt from the blue! My wife too! My wife!'

Then it had just been fear pure and simple. The boys, a pair of upstanding little politicians straight out of their father's mould, had just got the shits up and made themselves scarce. Understandable, but cowardly.

Tina, though, said firmly that it was no shame to be so frightened and that the norms of civilised existence no longer applied. The unfortunate thing was that most people's eyes were only being opened now. Those refugees from Eastern Hessen or from the area around the Biblis reactor had only just realised the truth, even though their position had been clear in every detail for years now, and anyone in the know could have told them what would happen in the case of armed conflict. As long as the awareness of a threat stayed short of actual experience, it remained inconsequential and could be suppressed. Under the Third Reich too, many had only joined the Resistance when defeat became inevitable. Perhaps Marc and Lukas had come to the same conclusion. Perhaps they had been able to show some element of resistance that they had always hidden before. Tina looked Petzold straight in the eye throughout. He just nodded dumbly, whether in agreement or perplexity it was impossible to tell.

Tina didn't persuade me, but Petzold seemed relieved.

Tina went on to say that we must have the courage to acknowledge our fear. Fear was often a good counsellor; real fear had a basis of truth. Heroes were usually terrible cowards. Germany has never been short of heroes, but it has always lacked people with civil courage. The worst cowards at the moment were the 'heroes' sitting in the government bunkers in the Eifel.

Petzold said his farewells and left as he had arrived, very depressed.

Tina and I often discuss our fear now. Where is the borderline, beyond which we are all alone? Tina says there is no such borderline, that love is stronger than fear or death. I don't know. But that experience will come soon. I admire Tina's ability to speak so calmly of death, despite the fact – or perhaps because? – the problem has become so concrete and immediate. We have agreed to keep the freedom of choosing our deaths. But I still have the sense of being an innocent man, waiting for death in a condemned cell. I doubt whether we have any way of imagining what lies ahead. But that is just what makes the fear even more intolerable.

Now, as ever, I still feel it is important to think through the question of whether this war is 'necesary' or even 'inevitable'. Kant said that questions of war or peace were decided by the interests – or whims – of our rulers. He lived in the age of absolutism, when the 'interests' of the state were largely identical with those of the reigning prince. He was convinced that if a republican form of government was introduced, war would be eliminated, or at least be possible only as defensive war. The masses did not want war, since the sacrifice they had to make was greater than any possible gain. People were peaceful and wanted peace, their 'masterpiece'. War was an action contrary to reason. Practical reason and ethical values were identical.

Freud thought differently. War was necessary, he thought, because society's suppression of natural instincts led to frustrations and aggressive feelings in individuals which sooner or later demanded an outlet. War was a consequence of cultural discipline and the socialisation process that we were all subjected to. Social disciplines, moral norms, the need for order, laws, punishment and reward, hierarchical divisions, authority, obedience, etc., were reinforced at the expense of our natural drives and needs, creating a strong superego but undermining the power of the autonomous self. A 'discontent with civilisation' was the result, meaning that the only real possibility for protest so far as the individual was concerned when he suffered injury and humiliation in the public sphere had to be confined to the private sphere. Thus psychological illnesses, though socially caused, remain a 'private matter'. If they manifest themselves as criminal acts – which means as unacceptable aggressive actions – then they are punished. The victim becomes victim twice over.

Freud therefore sees it as inevitable that some kind of safety-valve has to be provided for this suppressed aggression before it

81

becomes a danger to society – and the most effective safety-valve is war.

According to this interpretation, war has social causes within the framework of a repressive, paternalistic culture.

Marx stands somewhere between Kant and Freud. On the one hand, war is a result of capitalism's repressive, exploitative social structure, which is against the objective interests of the exploited, underprivileged workers but is accepted by them in both an active and a passive sense as 'fate', as long as the masses lack awareness of the underlying social causes. On the other hand, war is also a conscious tool of the 'small capitalist' class, which has taken over the state to secure its profit interests. Once the proletariat has taken over the power in society by a revolutionary act, which is the consummation of an inevitable social process, then war will disappear as a factor in human history.

Between Freud and Marx, there is plenty of explanation for the phenomenon of 1914, when the masses went to war in a storm of enthusiasm, in England and France as well as Germany. Frustrations, poverty, deprivations, political repression, the lack of outlets for a host of powerful subliminal drives, had all led to the 'discontent with civilisation' reaching such a pitch that a dangerous degree of suppression of aggression existed, which could easily have led to social upheavals and revolutions.

The manipulative factor appears simply because the egocentric drives (Kant: reason) have already been so weakened that a distorted view of reality has become possible. The repressed, depraved ego gives itself up to a kind of collective insanity. Killing, which had been forbidden by law, by morality, by social pressures, is now not just permitted but actually blessed and encouraged by the highest authorities in the state and society – as moral, ethically justifiable action. Feelings of guilt are suppressed by the individual's conviction that he is fighting for a good and just cause: the fatherland, religion, freedom, the defence of the homeland. And to fit into this, the enemy becomes 'evil' and 'inhuman.'

This was why young Englishmen could drop napalm bombs on young Argentines, while the British Conservatives were aiming to improve their election chances and the Argentine military rulers were looking to divert attention from their social failures; young Americans could massacre Vietnamese women and children, while for Washington's imperialism it was a question of its claim to world leadership; young Germans could massacre 'Bolsheviks' while the Nazis wanted 'living space' in the East; in 1914–18 the sons of peasants could ram bayonets into the bodies of the sons of workers, while for the coal barons and the financiers the target was the coal and iron mines in France and Belgium.

If those young people had met in a bar in time of peace, they would have cheerfully shared a few drinks and toasted each other's health.

Clausewitz feared the mass-based national armies, which could easily be misused in a welter of emotion. The possibility of such misuse endangers the function of war as a rational continuation of politics by other means. Moltke, however, considered war to be part of God's natural order for the world, peace to be a dream – and not even a beautiful one, at that.

Historically, Kant's hope has been proved futile. Is not the USA a democracy? And for all that, in this century it has conducted, induced, taken part in, intervened in, more wars than all the other industrial nations put together.

Even Freud's trust in the 'gentle but in the long run inevitable voice of reason' was proved misplaced. The fatal political, economic, ecological, technical, military, social, psychological consequences of modern industrial society, could not be controlled or mastered. Discontent with civilisation has never been stronger than in the past three decades, and never has our psychological deprivation been clearer, or our lack of perspective more meaningful, or the future blacker and more threatening, despite all our material prosperity.

And even Marx's ideas proved false in the light of reality. When socialism actually came into being, it did not dismantle the existing paternalistic structures, and discontent with civilisation (a communist one now) remained.

Never has aggression been a stronger factor in human relationships.

It is three in the morning, I cannot sleep, even though I am dead tired. My senses are wide awake, honed by danger. But I share this situation with others, with millions. We are not even granted individuality in our suffering. Collective suffering, mass fear. Mass death, produced by industrial methods and delivered in the same way. A product.

Hiroshima. It is not even fifty years since the first atom bomb exploded. The mushroom of flame and smoke that buried a hundred thousand human beings drew a vision of human annihilation in the sky over Japan. Anyone with the use of his rational faculty would have recognised a real watershed in the history of mankind. But only few were capable of that insight and also ready to draw the consequences: Einstein, Oppenheimer, Born. Too few. Nuclear weapons were made available as tools of political power, on the grounds that they could prevent what they could also cause: the destruction of the human race.

Hiroshima and Nagasaki were rebuilt – a fatal symbol. Today many military men and politicians are convinced that a world nuclear war is survivable and winnable. And that the sacrifices and costs are tolerable. Just as the victims of Hiroshima and Nagasaki were, when it came down to it, 'tolerable'. Human beings can be reproduced at will. The fact that the individual cannot only becomes clear when we die ourselves.

Deterrence. After Hiroshima, what was needed was for us to be deterred from developing nuclear weapons. The politicians created the bizarre phenomenon of deterrence *with* nuclear weapons.

The fateful mistake was to think that mere tools can make something happen, or prevent something from happening. All the weaponry that had been developed previously had carried its own imperatives that altered military strategy, determined defence policy and introduced new elements to politics. Those in responsible political and military positions could only bow to these imperatives, and yet they stuck to the delusion that they controlled the tools of war. But those tools controlled them and their policies.

Stone Age man, for example, had to adapt to the demands and 'imperatives' of the stone club, or the bow, or the throwing spear once he had discovered them – at the time for a very specific purpose.

No-one will dispute that scientific-technical progress is a

deterministic process that results from the physiological structure of the brain. Every 20,000 years, the volume of the brain increases by a cubic centimetre, its capacity for learning and storing information expands, its deductive capability increases. Historically this amounts to an explosion. Scientific and technical miracles are the result. Modern weapons systems are miraculous achievements of the brain.

But the emotional capacity of the human being, which is supposed to be located in the older, constant segments of the brain, is stagnating. Fear, hatred, distrust, envy, covetousness, the desire to kill, fanaticism, have not changed through the millennia. They find expression in a direct and violent way, hardly guided or controlled by intelligence, perception, consciousness, understanding or reason. Fear can make available the products of intelligence, such as weapons, and use them for destructive purposes, while our understanding can justify and rationalise the most barbaric orgies of killing. The same emotions that guided the use of the club in the Stone Age are now responsible for launching multi-warheaded ICBMs. No difference. A fatal bio-psychological contradiction in the human race. And it is threatening to destroy it.

Man is not the consummation of the creation but its most highly-developed problem. The intellect and its achievements have actually overloaded the human psyche. A faulty mutation? And we, while we are still breathing, feeling, alive, are witnessing the fact that nature is in the process of correcting that fault by extinguishing that species. Unfortunately we are being forced to experience this 'correction' in a very direct and lethal way.

The lesson of Hiroshima was not understood. The destruction of that city altered everything – except the way human beings think.

But at this moment the nations of the world do not want war. Fear is more potent than 'the discontents of civilisation'. Why does the catastrophe still appear to be unfolding with such inexorability? This is a war against people, against humanity, against the entire race of man.

Attempted to get into the office, but only got as far as the main station in Wiesbaden. End of the line there in more ways than one, no trains. It seemed that the railwaymen had not come to work either.

People were standing around in the street. They simply stood there, no purpose, no movement, no placards, no signs of protest. The ultimate form of begging for life. Silent, hangdog, resigned.

To Frankfurt by car. Special permit. A lot of troops on the autobahn, endless columns, predominantly American vehicles. Anxious faces under the steel helmets. Hanging grimly onto their automatic rifles. A few of the boys already with their faces blackened. Not really camouflage, more a wish to make themselves invisible. The magical function of the mask. Invulnerability.

Same at the Hauptwache, the Geotheplatz and the Zeil: silent, waiting masses of people. Almost as if in church. Silent prayer. *Kyrie eleison*, Lord have mercy.

It feels as if fate is playing a sadistic game with us: why is it that we are only grasping the nuclear threat now, when it seems inevitable? Why not four or five days ago? Why not months, years ago? The two most terrifying words of all: Too Late.

Nuclear reality has proved too much for human thought. It is impossible to think – or feel – in that kind of hyperlative extreme. Machine guns, tanks, artillery, aircraft, conventional carpet bombing as in Dresden or Hamburg, battles like Stalingrad or Monte Cassino, mass slaughter: still conceivable, within our capacity to experience without going mad. What is a ten megaton bomb, though? An abstraction! Terrible, of course – maybe twice a Hiroshima, four times a Dresden. But we can live with it . . . This abstraction is ten million tons of explosive. Packed with cubic centimetre sized 'bricks' that if put end to end would cover the distance from Frankfurt to San Francisco – 10,000 kilometres. Three times the explosive power of all the shells and bombs used during the entire Second World War. A futile attempt at description. A ten-megaton bomb remains an abstraction, because its dimensions are cosmic. Hell is unimaginable.

The failure of our imaginations and our conceptual abilities has benefited the politicians and the military men, who never possessed either of these in the first place. Instead, they have offered concepts that are at least within our capacity to understand: deterrence, prevention of war, defence, defensive capacity, freedom, balance of power. Defence Minister Wörner in 1983: 'He who wants to prevent war must have the capacity to fight one.' Of course. Anyone can understand that.

In the final analysis, the peace movement failed because it could not challenge the plausibility of such statements on the commonsense, everyday level that was necessary. Language can only handle concepts that come out of experience. Inferno, catastrophe, apocalypse: we think of Hiroshima, Dresden, the Second World War – and these words give no idea of what is actually coming. 'The destruction of humanity' is more than we can imagine. Inconceivable. And so it inspires no fear, or at least no fear that can be translated into political action. Enlightenment, the human race's transcending of its self-inflicted immaturity, has its limits.

Until just a few days ago, it would have been possible to prevent the government from joining in the preparations for this catastrophe. Through spontaneous general strikes and blockades. Now, however, the military machine is geared up and running on its own, without the people and, indeed, against the people.

Moltke: 'Eternal peace is a dream, and not even a beautiful one, and war is a part of God's world order. Within its framework we see unfolding the most noble virtues of man, courage and self-denial, duty, loyalty and self-sacrifice, the risking of our own lives. Without war, humanity would sink into a swamp of materialism.'

Ludendorff 45 years later: 'Total war demands that we possess the spiritual strength to overcome our own will to self-preservation.'

Goebbels fifteen years later: 'Do you want total war?'

Another 50 years later: Real total war, the last war in an infinite chain of wars, is an immediate prospect. Is as good as inevitable.

Early this afternoon, three gentlemen from the Ministry of the Interior and the Bureau for the Protection of the Constitution appear in the editorial office. Extremely polite officials. Once again, all talking of 'doing their job' and 'their instructions' – the famous little cogs who keep the machine in motion. They tell us that the situation demands that we avoid articles that might undermine our defensive capacity or disturb the public. Reader articles in particular, and features including comment. Our furious editor-in-chief asks: 'By what right?' Answer: 'We have our instructions! Emergency laws! You know, they were passed three years ago.' Especially to cover this eventuality. Foreseen, predicted, catered for. 'Gentlemen, please don't make things difficult.'

We feel humiliated, like children. Sense our impotence as journalists in three ways: by the presence of censors; by the fact that we tried to do the right thing, but too late; by the probability that even if we had done it in time it would have been ineffectual.

Now there is no difference to the situation under Ludendorff during the First World War. As he wrote in *Total War*: 'Strictest censorship of the press, stricter laws against the betrayal of military secrets, sealing of the borders, bans on meetings, imprisonment at least of the ringleaders among the "discontented". Close control of radio because "malcontents" or ill-intentioned saboteurs . . . will hinder the emergence of a popular will to fight, or even directly undermine it. It is also essential that we act with the utmost gravity and severity against these people. It is a matter of national preservation.'

The gentlemen sent by the government read this passage with great interest. After all, Ludendorff was one of our greatest generals. Along with Hindenburg, he beat the Russians at Tannenberg and brought the Russian steamroller to a halt at the Masurian Lakes.

The publishing board decided to continue to publish the paper, despite the censorship. Several colleagues of mine refuse to co-operate and go home.

It very quickly becomes clear that the three gentlemen

haven't much idea of what should be published and what not.

Why bother with news at all? Why have opinion and comment? All that's left of public opinion is prayer, hope and trembling.

Censors have obviously also been installed at the German newsagencies. The news coming through has been prettied up. The real situation is clear, however, from foreign agencies and radio reports, as well as from telephone discussions with our own correspondents.

The population of Eastern Hessen has meanwhile taken to the forests and the country roads, emptying entire towns and villages. Rumours: individual soldiers and entire units of the Bundeswehr have refused to use firearms to clear the blocked roads. Nevertheless, indescribable scenes. First attempts to push trucks into the ditches with heavy moving gear. Then the tanks simply kept on going, rolling over whatever was in their paths.

The people are going to be 'defended' like it or not, and any objections are being crushed with all force.

Tomorrow people will read in the paper: 'After some initial disturbance, the result of activities by saboteurs, the public is showing complete understanding for the units moving into their defensive positions.' The same rubbish on radio and television. Nothing but despicable collaborationism, all dancing to the same tune.

The editor-in-chief has moved out of his office. His cheeks red with impotent rage. If he had known this was coming a few days ago.

An attempt to catch up with some correspondence during the lunch hour was a failure. Every letter I could have written would have been a farewell or a note of condolence. But I read each letter avidly. The same despair! Is it worth communicating it back? I decide to force myself to write anyway. Just say that I am also rooted to the spot by fear and can't get out of it. Everyone understands that, and so we all understand each other, but this community of feeling still leaves us all alone. We all have to be like that Capuchin monk that I met at a magnificent monastery at Buxheim, in a fine church built by Dominikus Zimmermann: he was always ready. Whether it was to go to dinner or to die was unimportant to him. He was ready for anything at any time.

89

The government has indicated that an emergency evacuation plan is being considered, to get the population out of the 'endangered areas' in the south and west of the country. What idiocy. How are they going to evacuate ten million human beings in a few days? Hadn't they been able to foresee that the population wouldn't just stay put by their own firesides and die peaceful and uncomplaining? I try to imagine what was going on in the minds of those military men and politicians when they were dreaming up their 'defence scenarios'. They can't have wasted any thought on the populations of East Hessen, Lower Saxony and Northern Bavaria. Those ten million human beings must have been written off straight away as the price of freedom.

The censors demanded that we put together a story around the news that NATO had made a comprehensive offer of negotiations to the Warsaw Pact. To prevent things going to the brink. The current troop movements should be stopped and verifiable controls created, with the aim of withdrawing all military units from the areas within 80 kilometres of the GDR and Czechoslovakian borders.

We asked the gentlemen what the purpose might be of such an offer, which was obviously to be seen as a trust-creating exercise, when the build ups in the Near and Middle East were continuing and the Americans were in the process of breaking the last of the resistance on Cuba with napalm. Fighting was already going on in various areas of the world. The Soviets would clearly see the offer as a trick. It would tie down three million of their troops in Europe while the Americans continued to fight them in Ethiopia, North Yemen and Cuba. The withdrawal would amount to a unilateral measure.

The gentlemen from the government got their way. But they couldn't find anyone to write their commentary for them. The leader article eventually came in a telex direct from the Defence Ministry: calm, confidence in the authorities, necessary measures, allies loyally standing by us, freedom at stake. The censors even cut the sentence: 'We must see the present conflict situation through, so that the permanent, latent threat to the Free West under which we have lived for all these years can be ended.' My offer to write a piece on the anniversary of the dropping of the atomic bomb on Hiroshima was rejected.

The space-filler in the local news section reports yet again on the overflowing churches. People are crowding under the shadow of the cross, and everyone is wearing crucifixes. Priests are having to ask those attending services to make way for those waiting outside. The need for comfort is unquenchable. Most priests sharply criticising the politicians, defence experts, military leaders and the arms lobby. To threaten the use of nuclear weapons had been sin enough, but what was happening now amounted to blasphemy and a complete turning away from God. The church's time has come. It has the power to give comfort, or at least to grant people more of a sense of composure in the face of death. We can do neither. The government has issued a warning against subversive sermons.

Our overworked censors overlooked the report. I'm curious to see what they say tomorrow. If they find the time to appear tomorrow.

American Intelligence sources say that the Soviet missile units in Eastern Siberia have been placed on full combat alert. The target chosen for the new SS-20-As can only be Japan. The White House has warned the Soviets not to undertake any further escalations of the conflict. To everyone's complete surprise, China has announced its strict neutrality, though its missiles are also on full alert. Concern in the West about whether China will swing right onto the Kremlin's side, since the Chinese Chief of the General Staff has apparently made energetic demands for such a move: in view of the inevitable showdown between socialism and capitalism, there could be no doubt where China stands, he maintains.

The Soviet strategic submarines have set course for home, complete with their thousands of nuclear warheads. It is easier to protect them from American anti-submarine technology once they are within Soviet coastal waters, and it makes no difference to their capacity to reach any part of the USA with their missiles. There is no doubt that the Soviet mobilisation is in full swing. From the Kremlin's point of view, this is an absolute necessity. Moscow feels itself encircled by 400 American bases, from which it could be attacked at any time. The Americans hold all the best cards, can open up theatres of war at will, launch surprise attacks. The Soviet situation, and the Soviet defensive concepts, must be so complex that despite improved and centralised leadership, co-ordinated military operations on the scale necessary must seem near enough impossible. Thus there is a growing danger that nuclear weapons will be used quickly. It is now obvious that the Soviet Union could never have had wideranging offensive ambitions, because of its unfavourable geostrategic position.

On the other hand, the USA has no real capability of increasing the size of its army when required. A professional army has a disadvantage: a lack of reservists. The Soviets' unfavourable situation and the Americans' inability to make good human losses turns the use of nuclear weapons from a possibility to an inevitability.

Uli Löwith points out that my worst fears have not yet been realised. The Soviets have not yet attacked the Pershing and Cruise Missile bases. Despite the risk that the Americans could strike first, they are keeping their powder dry. It is therefore not out of the question to believe that both sideesss are aware of the risks they are running. Perhaps deterrence is still working, despite everything. Clutching at straws. Hope is the only way out for people like Uli – otherwise how could they tolerate sitting under the sword of Damocles and watching the thread getting thinner all the time?

The threat comes from outside. All the theatres of war have become one. The question is no longer whether there is any cause for war in Europe. The *casus belli* is the weapons the weapons themselves. They cry out for a showdown war, because their entire development is based on such a possibility. All that the political and military leaders can do is to make that showdown a reality.

What irresponsible dilettantism on the part of us Europeans, allowing ourselves to become such complete hostages of the two superpowers. Since 1984, all we have been able to do is pray that the two of them don't come into armed conflict somewhere in the world, because the moment they do, we inevitably get drawn right in – against our will, against our interests, but without a chance of defending ourselves by military means. For years, Bonn has sold our dependency on the USA as 'teaming up with the Americans' strategic potential'. The deterrent factor was supposedly increased thereby. With the introduction of the Pershings, the USA was 'guaranteeing the security of Europe at the price of its own national existence'. From time to time, the men in the White House must have simply burst out laughing at those stupid Europeans. The Americans never even considered allowing anyone else to limit their options, or stopping them from using the Pershings, MXes, Midgetmen, Tridents, or such-like missiles exclusively in their own interests. We just took it on faith that they would protect us. But how? As if any US president would sacrifice his own country for the sake of Europe? And why should he, when Europe will no longer exist? How do you protect a dead friend?

By stationing these damned missiles in Europe, the Americans were taking no risks at all – 'use them or lose them, we'll see' was the motto – but for Europeans the risk was total.

The Soviets can make the calculation that the Americans won't launch a single MX if they eliminate the Pershing and Cruise bases here. All reasonable assumptions now count against us: the short flight time of the missiles, their accuracy, the first-strike and 'beheading' options, and the threat that NATO – which means the USA – cannot allow itself to be predictable so far as the Soviets are concerned. What else can the Soviets do but to strike first, if they don't know what American intentions are? The Politburo in Moscow is prepared to commit suicide. But only after the Europeans have been sacrificed.

Both the alliance systems are tailored exclusively to the needs of the two superpowers. The allies are merely cannon-fodder, missiles fodder, battlegrounds. It is not as if the NATO states and the Warsaw Pact states sit in different boats. The non-nuclear powers are all sitting together in Charon's punt, ready to cross over to the underworld: Germans, Dutch, Belgians, Italians, English and Poles, Czechs, Hungarians and Bulgarians. The two big boys are also sitting in one boat, but each in another and alone. When ours has sunk, they can still get together and save their own skins if they choose.

The fate of the earth depends on a few men who have no way back. And so does mine as I sit here at my desk and vent my helplessness in this diary. People usually get to read diaries after the author's death. No one will ever read my diary.

93

Nature's try at creating a thinking being is ending in a totally banal fashion. With crimes that are greater than the men who commit them. The biggest crime possible is being committed by men who are not criminals at all, just morally and intellectually bankrupt. The last man alive on this planet will probably be a policymaker who will mutter haltingly: 'According to our calculations, this should never have happened.'

Nuclear weapons targeting computers make no distinctions between women and children, sick and old people, good and bad, peaceful and aggressive people, easterners and westerners, socialists and capitalists, religious individuals and unbelievers. Once the war machine has begun to move, there are only preprogrammed targets and enemies that have to be eliminated. Millions of people and their fates become no more than an abstraction, opposing resources and potentials.

The military leaders and politicians on both sides ought to be condemned to watch the inferno they are in the process of unleashing, over and over again and into eternity.

We cobbled a paper together. But our censors worked hard, and there were white spaces, even though every page had an ad for our own paper on it. One of the censors finally fished a prepared article out of his briefcase which dealt with the excellent UN convention concerning the protection of the world's cultural heritage. The frontline commanders on both sides had carefully prepared lists and were aware that they were not allowed to destroy important cultural monuments.

A macabre joke? It brought the first real laughter in the office for days, a brief liberation, even though for most of us it died on our lips pretty quickly.

The gentlemen from the government were embarrassed, it is true, but we journalists saw our chance. Karl Wieners offered to write a short opinion piece on the subject, which they hastily accepted.

Wieners wrote: It was noteworthy, and a hopeful indication of humane values on both sides that they had agreed not to destroy each other's museums, baroque churches, and Gothic cathedrals. After a war, the morale of the decimated populace would assuredly be raised by the existence of these monuments. Standing amidst the prevailing sense of gloom, they would not

94

only symbolise the good old times but would also act as a harbinger of better times to come. Cultural monuments are known for their long life, which is not true of human beings. Human beings are unfortunately not considered cultural monuments and are therefore not seen as worthy of protection. What does it matter in the sight of eternity whether a man lives twenty or eighty years?

Moreover, and again in contrast to our cultural heritage, human beings can be reproduced at will – so long as just a few survive – a fact which immediately reduces their inherent value. Since Adam and Eve, no human being has been indispensable.

After finishing work, we stayed together to drink a beer or two. The general air of depression had become chronic. Just about everyone felt they had given as much as they could. It was hard to imagine how under the same circumstances we had once cracked jokes, laughed, argued, debated. When Charlie asked 'What are you going to do, boys?' we just shrugged, stared into our beer glasses. But his simple question was like an arrow in the heart. Fear sat heavy and cold in our stomachs and gradually took our breath away from us.

Once one is alone, the thought of the end becomes more concrete. In the presence of friends, it seems absurd. They are still healthy and unharmed, they are tangible. The thought that we could all soon look like the victims of Hiroshima – our skin bursting with sores, our eyeballs evaporated, limbs broken or dying from unstaunchable internal bleeding – remains nothing more than macabre theory.

Hardly any of us will be coming into work tomorrow. No one wants to work under censorship. Let them make their own newspapers. The whole thing has been pointless for a long time now, in any case.

Drawn-out farewells. Between rushes of our own fear, there is still room for sympathy with friends. Embraces. 'All the best, and be happy!'

On the drive home, I all but hit a military truck.

I can feel myself all churned up inside. The extinction will be total, not a trace left behind, even in memory. No one who will remember me. To have to accept that one will be simply extinguished is debilitating, because it has no sense, because nothing new will come of it. Like a slaughtered animal. Such an animal dies without dignity, as a commodity for someone else's purposes. We shan't even have a function as commodity or purpose. We shan't even have that much sense of worth. To be so lost, and to lack the power to lament, to accuse.

6th August, midnight

As evening drew on, strangers turned up in Taunusrodt, including many small children. They came from the direction of Idstein, exhausted and hungry, with the children practically dropping out of their arms. They said they had found their way through from the vicinity of Bad Neustadt and Mellrichstadt. Why? Because there were signs of war everywhere. They had driven off the night before but had soon ended up in a traffic jam. Bundeswehr and American patrols were not letting anyone through, said one thin, rangy man without emotion, as if it were something quite natural. So they had just carried on on foot, always heading westwards, away from the war. They had not wanted to go into Frankurt.

Well, what now? Mayor Hofmann, who had been fetched to settle the matter, swung between irritation, as if he was faced with gypsies, and a sense that a real human tragedy was unfolding here. Did they have any money? They could live in the inn. They had their savings with them, the thin man said, and pulled his wallet out of his pocket, as if to show his credentials. But the money would not last too long. They were refugees, he said, as if refugee status was already an established fact in Germany. It had been impossible to stay where they had been. Soldiers everywhere, everywhere weapons, guns, tanks. It wasn't hard to see what was coming. In the end they were shown to the *White Hart* inn. Hofmann intends to bring the matter up in the village council in the morning. He was visibly perplexed. It was obvious that these were not just tourists visiting Taunusrodt for pleasure. But were they really 'refugees' at this stage?

96

The first air raid warning. The sirens in Taunusrodt sound almost quaint and cosy. Nevertheless, we rushed down into the cellar while bombers screamed over the village at low altitude, heading east. Tornados belonging to the Bundeswehr's air force.

We learned the reasons for the alert an hour later. The first nuclear bombs have been dropped! The Americans and the Soviets are fighting with nuclear weapons. The threshold has been crossed. The doorway to Armageddon has been kicked open. Deterrence has failed. The drama called 'Humanity' has entered its last act. A short one. I don't think I drew breath once while I listened to the news on the BBC.

The Americans used tactical nuclear weapons to wipe out the Soviet bases in North Yemen and Ethiopia. They are also threatening to use nuclear weapons to halt the Soviet advance in Pakistan. There are rumours that Soviet airborne troops have occupied the major oilfields in Saudi Arabia. Units of the US Rapid Intervention Force are said to have also landed in the country.

The Soviets were not slow to exact a terrible retribution. Or were they the first to resort to nuclear arms? The US base on Diego Garcia was wiped off the face of the earth, along with the island, by two Soviet SS-20 missiles. Okinawa and Subic Bay are also said to have gone. Huge losses.

Soviet bridgehead on Hokkaido. The 'unsinkable aircraft carrier' called Japan is being boarded. The Japanese airforce was destroyed in a matter of hours. In retaliation, the Americans are attacking Soviet bases on the island of Sakhalin.

Now there can be no more doubt that the war will spread to Europe. The fatal logic of nuclear weaponry: they can end a localised war with one blow, and so they constantly need new local theatres of war. Ethiopia and North Yemen, Diego Garcia, Subic Bay and Okinawa have all been taken off the map. When a nuclear bomb explodes, the war is over. For ever.

Any attempts to carry through military operations with conventional weapons or to win victories in that way can be nullified in a matter of minutes. Conventional armies have lost all use – except to act as the tripwire before the nuclear strike. The conventionally 'victorious' army creates its own destiny, and at the same time visits that destiny upon the land in which it is fighting. But conventional war is now no more than a ritual, a prelude to the nuclear strike, perhaps of value as an excuse.

Why does this realisation only come in the wake of an insane experiment such as this? So far as Europe is concerned, the examples of Ethiopia, Diego Garcia, Yemen and Okinawa ought to be enough. One experiment is enough. We ought to be able to say: now stop, withdraw the troops, halt the military buildup and put it into reverse. There is nothing to be gained from a military point of view now.

Too late. Europe has abdicated all responsibility for itself. It has offered itself to the superpowers as an experimental laboratory and seems set to play this role with a kind of bizarre pleasure right to the end. I am forced to think of Thomas Mann's *Letters of Those About to Die*, where he writes: 'We live in a world whose intellectual and moral bankruptcy is such that its fate is being entrusted to destructive weapons of horrifying efficiency, which are being stockpiled to the tune of the idiotic threat "if we must, so be it" – where the only end result of such a threat will be to transform the earth into a desert shrouded in poisonous mists.'

7th August, evening

It was only late this afternoon that we learned that the Steffenhagen family committed suicide last night. Four children, the oldest twelve and the youngest seven months old. Steffenhagen was a teacher. A good friend of mine. No suicide note, but everyone is aware of the motive. The first people in the village to take that way out. Depression and once again a raging anger. The blood of that family is on the hands of those political criminals! Tears well in my eyes, and I feel hatred and a desire to kill. What a joy it would be to have a machine gun and to have all those bureaucrats, advisers, politicians, military leaders, defence experts, standing in front of me. Impotent fantasies that do nothing to free me of this burden. Senseless self-

98

flagellation. I feel like shouting for help, and find myself choking on this sense of helplessness.

Tina's spiritual strength seems inexhaustable. But I can see that she is mobilising her final reserves. There is infinite sadness in her face, and her eyes have lost their sparkle.

7th August, midnight

Is it true that elitist attitudes are inherited, a function of some socio-cultural genetic patterning? A common feature: wars tend to be conducted most ruthlessly and with the greatest possible brutality when it has been made clear in advance that the victorious élite will eliminate the defeated one. This was the rule for thousands of years. The victor would ruthlessly destroy the nobility and the ruling class of the defeated tribes and nations, banish them or sell them into slavery. In Imperial Rome, the sons of princes fought as gladiators in the arenas.

The victor was forced to act in this way, because only the nobility was capable of organising a people into military action. As long as a ruling class existed, it constituted a threat to the conqueror. To be generous in victory was dangerous sentimentality. The nobility on both sides were well aware of the fate that awaited them if they lost, and so they fought to the end. It was better to die on the battlefield than to be executed, or left to rot in a dungeon, or end your days in slavery. The ruling élite had everything to lose in war: power, authority, property and physical existence. The ruling class *was* the fatherland. As late as the eighteenth century, the ideas of 'nation' and 'nobility' were synonymous. The French revolutionaries beheaded 'the nation'. 'Lovely it is and honorable to die for one's country' expresses the interests of the élite, not those of the people. Total war also means total victory and total gain. The prospect of these compensated for the risks of war.

The Egyptians massacred the Nubian tribal princes along with their families, and the people of Israel slaughtered the aristocracy of conquered nations, while the Romans sold captured Thracian, Parthian or German nobles into slavery or, like Caesar in Gaul, made short shrift of them. Charlemagne had

99

the entire Saxon aristocracy beheaded at Verden on the Aller. The first thing the Spanish conquistadores did was to get the Indian princes within their power.

It was only when the European nobility began to realise the danger of mutual extermination that war became more 'civilised'. Surrender became a realistic option, and to arouse bloodlust in an army became not just a crime but an act of punishable stupidity. A new one could be created out of what was left over. But Hobbes described very accurately the way in which kings and princes constantly eyed each other, suspicious as gladiators. 'They keep their weapons directed against each other and do not let each other out of their sight, they have their fortresses, garrisons and guns on the borders of their empires and their constant spies in their neighbours' lands. This is a warlike attitude.' It may well also have been a kind of deterrence, but it was ineffective when there was a chance of victory. And that chance always existed.

Hitler and the Nazis reintroduced the barbaric practice of extermination. It was not only Jews who were systematically and ruthlessly liquidated, but also the Polish and Soviet-communist élites. It was a total struggle for existence between irreconcilable élites that had also succeeded in securing the support of their people (a relatively easy task for the conquered nations, since Hitlerian barbarism also threatened the masses' existence). Once the tide turned against it, the Nazi élite fought to the very last, to the point of total exhaustion.

Now, once again, two irreconcilable élites are facing each other. The existence of one signifies a threat to the existence of the other. Both ruling classes, the communist *nomenklatura* and the managerial élite in the capitalistic industrial nations, know that at the very least their authority and their privileges would be swept away if the other ever emerged victorious from a war. They probably also have reason to fear for their physical existence. The lives of the likes of Agnelli, Rothschild, Flick, von Finkh, Thurn and Taxis, Morgan, Rockefeller, du Pont, and all the presidents, ministers, chairmen, bosses or owners would seem meaningless and no longer worth living, as would those of Honecker, Husak, Shivkov, Ceauçescu, Andropov, Chernenko and all the countless privileged members of the opposing élite.

100

That is why they are prepared to run the ultimate risk – that of total war. They would rather be destroyed than submit to the mercies or otherwise of a victor. The difference between them and earlier élites is that they possess total weapons, which will enable them to drag their peoples with them to destruction.

When I was travelling on the subway in Moscow or visiting the Bolshoi Theatre, it seemed to me absurd to consider conducting war with nuclear missiles against these people, of exterminating them. I remember a Soviet journalist spontaneously making the same comment as we strolled across the Zeil in Frankfurt. Now this absurdity is becoming reality. But the actual people are not involved. Just a handful of technicians, engineers and missile specialists will unleash the inferno, with their orders coming from a very few military commanders, who will be given the signal by five or six politicians. There will not even be armies involved.

It is not so strange that élites should seem possessed by some collective deathwish, at least in times of political failure. They feel that they are at the end of their tethers and unable to see their way forward: the ecological disaster, the catastrophe of the Third World, the chronic social crisis with its massive unemployment, the twenty wars and military conflicts currently raging in the world, the collapse of social consensus, dissatisfaction, resistance, apathy, criminality, hooliganism, drug addiction, need for metaphysical comfort and irrational loss of self, the psycho-social illnesses, fear of the future, failure of perspective, a sense of futility, isolation, loneliness. A predatory civilisation without a sense of common humanity. What does it actually exist for?

A threat that we have created for ourselves is interpreted as an external one and projected onto an opponent, who is seen as having brought about the present hopeless situation by his diabolical, coldly calculated plotting. Couldn't we have solved all our problems by now if it hadn't been for the Communist danger? If that hadn't existed, then we should have been able to use all those billions spent on armaments for humanitarian purposes. And to the Communist *Nomenklatura*, all the ills of their world seem to have been caused by an aggressive bourgeois élite which has now reached the inevitable end of its power and is

101

fighting for its very life. This atmosphere of finality brings out a deathwish, a kind of brotherhood with the enemy in the act of joint self-immolation.

Nations defend themselves differently. History knows many successful efforts of collective self-defence. The Spaniards against Napoleon, the French, Norwegians, Jugoslavs, Ukrainians and White Russians against Hitler, Gandhi's Indians against the British, the people of Mexico, Cuba or Nicaragua against blood thirsty dictators, the Vietnamese against the Americans, were all fighting for freedom pure and simple. People will only fight for that. But their defence makes sense and is voluntary. They are fighting for their freedom, and that of each individual. A people's fight for liberation requires more of a kind of civil courage from each individual involved than any readiness to exterminate an enemy in the military sense. The desire for collective suicide is alien to the masses.

We Germans have always lacked civil courage. We have never been short of military bravery.

– I think of the old innkeeper in a village near Clermont-Ferrand and of the old ticket seller in the 'Museum of the Great Patriotic War in Minsk'. Both had been resistance fighters and both agreed in saying: 'Do you know what the worst thing was when we took German soldiers prisoner? So long as they were lying there opposite us in their grey uniforms, firing away, we could shoot back without a thought. But when we saw them standing before us, and we pulled the helmets off their heads, they were suddenly just children, young lads, trembling with fear. But we had to shoot them. Yes, sir, we had to kill them! We simply couldn't allow even one of them to live, because that would have been suicidal for us. But everyone tried to avoid being involved in the executions. We had to draw lots every time, and those who lost wouldn't speak for days afterwards. It was terrible!'

There is brutality in a people's way of liberation. But there is also human sympathy.

· The people is an indispensable part of this form of defence.

But such a degree of readiness to defend ourselves is only possible under other social and political conditions. A society worth defending, one in which a sense of social justice and

102

solidarity had enforced basic reforms, would have placed the privileges of the élite in jeopardy.

Now we are about to die for freedom, a freedom which is the property of an élite ruling class – and on the other side for socialist achievements that are the privileges of another élite ruling class.

Montesquieu, Rousseau, Kant, Lessing, Thomas Abbot and the early democrats were probably right in their conviction that war would become impossible and disappear from history if the republican form of government was established, since the masses, which would then be sovereign, have no interests in war, which always leaves them the losers. Marx thought the same way: the rule of the people would mean the end of war. Fatally for us, all we have done is change élites.

8th August, mid-day

Sunday. The last we shall live through? What a week, taking me from desparate hope to impotent despair. It looks as though the end of the world can no longer be stopped. The worst thing is knowing the way the course of the catastrophe has been pre-planned and thus being aware of the tiny possibilities of stopping it. We have to give up hoping for reason to gain the upper hand, then things become easier. To deliver ourselves up to fate could turn despair and fear into resignation. This would silence all protest. Instead, I prefer to keep rebelling.

I have a longing for peace that must resemble that of an old person. To be eighty or ninety now, living with the awareness of death's imminence – and to be able to shake my head at these young people's inconceivable stupidity. To be incapable of being affected, to have already taken my leave of life. But what is threatened now is not just the physical liquidation of the human race – the death of an individual five billion times over – but the extinction of the intellect and the ethical sense on this planet.

Weigand made the Steffenhagens' suicide the centrepiece of his sermon. The service was full to overflowing, Tina says. Some of us, he said, die of physical illnesses or wounds, and some of

103

spiritual wounds. The Steffenhagens had not been able to bear this world any longer, and had chosen that way to protest. It would not be up to us humans, but to God, to decide whether the parents had been right in making that decision for their four children as well.

There is a sense of certainty that the Steffenhagens have chosen the better way.

During her holiday in France, Christine read in a book by Julien Green that every individual human being is the cause of war. And therefore everyone has the power to stop it. 'When we try to find the causes of war elsewhere than in our own hearts, we become ensnared in a maze of human sophistry, for war is predominantly a human drama.'

At first I felt to dismiss the quotation out of hand, for Green was a very spiritual writer with a delight in metaphysical symbolism, but then I understood the enormity of his words: there is no better description of determinism. Since the power of the individual to end a way has previously only become effective when it was clear that there would be a winner or a loser, this means that a nuclear must lead to the destruction of all of us, since the 'victor' is also condemned to death. This, of course, is the fatal flaw: since the world's leaders have no experience of nuclear war, they will act according to traditional notions and attempt to win a 'victory'. But nuclear weapons do not permit any such thing as a victor. Only losers, victims. Bismarck said that war is too important to leave to the soldiers. Nowadays we can say: Peace is too important to leave to the politicians.

Lunch on the terrace. Chattering swallows above us. A mellow, blue day, nature's gift to life. I miss Andreas terribly. If need be, I shall order him to come home.

8th August, midnight

Meaningless, sanitised news on German ARD radio. When the Chancellor was introduced yet again. I turned to another station. Intolerable. Radio Bern reports further Soviet advances in Pakistan and Iran. Moscow and Washington are each accusing the other of having been first to use nuclear weapons. Each

104

rejects the other's accusations and refers to 'a grave precedent'. Both maintain that the other bears responsibility for further developments.

Strict martial law in Japan. The Americans are landing troops on Taiwan and reinforcing their bases in Oman and Somalia. Oman and Somalia are protesting and have stated that this is happening against their wills. Both countries abrogated their treaties allowing US bases on 4th August. Their protests are understandable, because now both countries face the threat of nuclear extinction. It only takes two hours to reprogramme a Soviet SS-20-A onto another target.

The American Chief of General Staff is complaining about his acute lack of manpower. The US can no longer live up to its treaty agreements. According to NATO's logic, this means that tactical nuclear weapons will be used when conventional forces can no longer take the strain. Goldsmith has recommended padding out US units with troops from the allied ASEAN countries and at the same time calling up American veterans.

Emergency measures in the USA as well. The first indications of unrest among the population there. The authorities are making every effort to avert a mass exodus from the cities. One possible fatal result: panic reactions in the USA could drive the politicians and military leaders to take hasty measures, to try to win the 'race' against collapse on the home front by a rapid military decision. Everything is happening too late, a few days too late. But surely all this can't really be happening!

Is the Soviet leadership under similar pressure?

9th August, evening

Spent the entire day wandering around Wiesbaden. A ghost town. Only a few people on the streets, and despite the continuing hot weather the Kurpark is desolate. Only a few old people, strolling with every appearance of serenity.

The life of the city has almost been extinguished. Hardly any cars, only a few buses. Most shops and banks closed, many of them like fortresses with their windows barred. A lot of drunks.

105

As if clearing their systems of the fear that is hardly distinguishable from the air we breathe.

A moving experience in the Friedrichstrasse: a procession of about sixty men and women of various ages, each dressed in a sack and with his or her face covered in white chalk. Heads bowed, walking around with their arms tight by their sides, murmuring some sing song litany. The upper parts of their bodies swayed rhythmically from side to side. I became aware of how natural this scene seemed. In 'normal' times we would have said: a bunch of neurotics indulging themselves. Now they are probably an expression of normality, people who have succeeded in dealing with the situation better than the rest of us.

A woman was preaching doom in front of the Bonifazius Church. A voice that carried well, had an edge of sharpness, though it was not loud. Thin, about forty-five, a black dress that was too big for her. She had an audience of some 200 people, waiting to be allowed into the church. They were listening in silence while the woman told them about the end of the world. No one was obviously listening to her, but neither was anyone protesting against her activities. Again the scene seemed natural. After some hesitation, I overcame my resistance sufficiently to go up to the woman and whisper in her ear that she should not preach the end of the world but the return of Christ. She just stared right past me with eyes sad as death.

The mind cannot stand the pressure of such a fear of death any longer and reacts with confusion. Protest, even if it is futile. But it does help, I believe, and above all it is a normal reaction to what is happening. The desire to gain entry to another world. Another world, not a better one. Any other is better.

The air raid shelter in the Schwalbacher Strasse is still empty. If the worst happens, better to wait for a quick death in one's own apartment.

Prisoners from Latin-American states all agree in saying that one of the cruellest tortures is to be beaten while blindfold, because it is impossible to prepare yourself for the blow. Not only is the pain doubled or trebled, but the will to resist is shattered. You know that the blow will come, but not when or where. The entire body spasms in on itself, and the victim quickly has a feeling of going crazy. During this type of torture there has been the highest incidence of fatal circulatory collapses, though the blows in themselves should not warrant death.

Exactly our present situation.

Standing room only in the Marktkirche, no room to kneel. Only a few tears, but a lot of prayers mumbled into cupped hands.

The obviously exhausted priest recalled that human beings have always put themselves into situations of extremity with regard to death. At heart, this was our destiny. There has always been plenty of room for hell on earth. For those millions who came to Auschwitz, the world ended as soon as they arrived on the notorious platform. They had already been forced to give up hope before they took off their clothes to enter the gas chambers, and they knew it.

Many of the concentration camp inmates nevertheless did not abandon their courage. Just when we have given up hope, it can happen that we gain courage, for it is then that we realise God is at our side. The life of man is not ended when death comes. God does not allow death to have the last word. Christians always live in hope of life. And in contrast to the victims of Auschwitz, we could still hope that this cup of sorrow would pass by us and humanity. It was in the hands of God to deflect those in power from their blind actions

On the other hand, it was also true that God had allowed mankind a high measure of freedom. We all had to ask ourselves whether we had accepted that responsibility. Had we not all been long astray? Had we really tried to take responsibility for the world and shape it as Christians? Had not each of us lived for himself and filled his days with easy superficialities, far from any deeper thought, far from our neighbours, far from God? Perhaps the present hour of need and despair should be interpreted as a warning to mend our ways at last.

The priest said all this without blame or accusation, but kindly and soothingly. Not a word about guilt or punishment, and therefore nothing about forgiveness – only about an open door through which anyone could enter and be welcome inside.

By the time he blessed the congregation, he had achieved a lot. I also felt strengthened.

Outside the sun was dazzling.

More refugees in Taunusrodt. Two families from Mainz were sent back immediately.

9th August, midnight

The committee of the Social-Democratic Party is demanding a unilateral withdrawal of NATO troops to sixty kilometres from the border. The risk entailed in this gesture was one that had to be taken. We could no longer cling to military principles such as that of the forward defence. We had to give the other side an indication of reasonableness, in the hope that they would understand and act on it. It was the only chance of averting a catastrophe of inconceivable proportions. The Federal Government should be aware of the special responsibility that it held in view of the fatally exposed position of the Federal Republic, and should make energetic representations to our allies in favour of this 'premeditated withdrawal'. It was not time to de-escalate rather than escalate. The committee recalled Kurt Schumacher's words from 1950: 'Europe cannot be America's forward line of defence, and Germany cannot fulfil the same function to Europe. No country can be made to serve the defensive purposes of others. Any system of military defence is possible only on the basis of mutuality.'

The German Confederation of Trade Unions has declared 'with the unanimous support of all its member unions' that a general strike will be considered if the Federal Government fails to make clear to its allies that de-escalating measures must be taken. After all, the confederation maintains, there is no indication of any kind that an attack on Europe is among the Soviet Union's primary objectives. The deadly danger we were currently facing was rather the result of the irresponsible politics of confrontation being conducted by the superpowers in other areas of the world, which was now threatening to encroach on Europe by a terrible process of contamination. There were no rational grounds for a totally exterminatory war in Europe. The danger that had now become apparent threatened the libertarian legal order in the Federal Republic, to which the unions felt themselves dutybound. If these demands by the unions were not fulfilled, they would call an indefinite general strike with immediate effect.

Urgent warnings from the leaderships of the churches also. The Council of the Evangelical Churches has demanded that the Federal Government take control of the Pershing-II sites.

The government has 'emphatically rejected' all these demands. We could not, it says, endanger the unity and determination of the Western Alliance at this difficult time. That would be suicide. The government has warned the unions about a general strike. According to the emergency legislation currently in force, this would be high treason and would be prevented by all means available.

Also a sharp rejoinder to the 'irrational demands of the Evangelical Churches' Council'.

I don't know whether to laugh or cry. As always the social democrats and the unions have missed their opportunity. A determined stance when it's already too late. Their failure is the tragedy of the German people.

Finally I feel nothing but a dull despair.

I am frightened of sleep. It brings terrible dreams.

10th August, mid-day

An announcement by the Federal Government that absence from places of work will no longer be considered acceptable. Absence without excuse will lead to immediate dismissal. Severe measures threatened against government employees especially. The paralysis of public transport systems is actually a real disaster. Banks and shops are being forced to open. The country is paralysed and is all but in a state of general strike even without the social democrats and the union. It is more like a general refusal . . . The public is over-stressed, reduced to a state of stunned inaction by the constant air raid warnings.

The threat of apocalypse and the fear that results are not going to be dispelled by government threats. This time German discipline is not enough.

Hardly any troop movements any more. The autobahn between Cologne and Frankfurt is like a graveyard, only a few military vehicles. The build ups on both sides are over, and the soldiers are standing with their weapons at the ready. Instead there is the constant roar of fighter planes overhead. Showing the flag. Europe is ready for the leap into the abyss.

Another dazzling summer's day. The people of Taunusrodt are lured out of their homes and shelters. Stand around in discreetly gossiping groups. Extreme ups and downs in mood. Where there's life there's hope . . . even on the edge of the grave, we keep planting seeds of hope. Excluding the Steffenhagens, of course. Can a policy that has conjured up this insane threat now find a way out? Perhaps self-deterrence still works. That would be a miracle.

Christine gives me hope, for she is young. Ralf says that for the first time in days he feels an easing in his chest. I am having to take myself in hand, so that my face does not betray how I feel inside. Just to be free of fear for a few moments would be a relief.

What would happen if the danger really was averted? Would the people force a new defence policy on its rulers? Would the sick joke of nuclear deterrence be ended? A restructuring of the Bundeswehr, civil defence? It is far more probable that the apologists of the present policy would see themselves confirmed in their beliefs and would claim that everything has functioned superbly. The West stayed tough, and the Soviets gave in. So let's have more of the same.

Nevertheless, nuclear war has now become conceivable. We have experienced a fraction of what it is. But the fear and the memory will not last very long. It will be suppressed like a nightmare. How quickly the horrors of the Second World War receded into the background, how easily even the generation who had experienced it directly shrugged off its full meaning. European civilisation is a civilisation based on war. The inability to mourn. Ability to live with war. Nowhere else except in the Federal Republic have I so often heard the phrase: 'Living with the nuclear bomb'.

A beautiful dream: the peoples of East and West unite to become one huge European peace movement that tears down the barriers between the two power blocs. We share our experiences of the shock of the past few days. A great feeling of solidarity

110

with each other, with nature, with the Third World, with mankind. Dismantling of deterrence as a system, with its lethal wrong-headedness and immorality. After this experience, it will be sufficient deterrent to realise that we were actually prepared to exterminate those 'hostile' people. The future principle of deterrence in a new world order must be that 'the real pain for a human being is not that which he suffers, but that which he inflicts' (Alessandro Manzoni).

Unfortunately this is a typical 'war dream'. Every generation has dreamed while the war was on. Nothing is more easily forgotten than the dreams dreamed in the midst of war.

An internationally-agreed, binding convention that decisions on war or peace be subjected to plebiscites on both sides.

10th August, evening

A sensation! It could mean the turning point! We are saved! The social-democratic governments in Holland and Denmark have declared their neutrality! Dutch troops are being withdrawn from Lower Saxony, the port of Rotterdam has been closed to American military shipments. Units of the Dutch army have occupied the Cruise Missile sites. The missiles must be removed from Dutch territory immediately. The Danish war fleet has been ordered to return to its territorial waters. Both governments have ceased all co-operation in the work of NATO headquarters and its regional commands. Mass expressions of delight in Denmark and the Netherlands.

Gloom in Washington and in the bunker in the Eifel! The American president has referred to a stab in the back for the Western Alliance that will have grave consequences. The Federal Government is obviously anxious to keep the American's trust. Has also, of course, spoken of stab-in-the-back and betrayal. Comment on radio and television: A lot of talk about the cowardice of the Dutch and the Danes, their betrayal, their attempt to save their own skins. Social democrats can never be relied on. Should have known.

The Hague and Copenhagen have stated that NATO is a defensive alliance, formed only to avert the danger posed by clear

111

Soviet aggressive intentions in Europe. Such aggressive intentions are not discernible at the moment. The present dangerous situation has arisen solely because of a policy of confrontation between the USSR and the USA in theatres of war in other parts of the world. The governments of Holland and Denmark could assume no responsibility for that policy of confrontation. They were not even involved. It could not be in the interests of the allies of either of the superpowers to be held responsible for a policy over which they had no influence, which was directed against their interests, and which was being played out outside the sphere of either alliance system. Both governments also appealed to the allies of the Soviet Union to free themselves from involvement with a policy of confrontation that was moving Europe and the world rapidly towards catastrophe and was therefore against the vital interests of the people of Eastern Europe as well. The task of the allies of both superpowers in the present crisis was to act as mediators

I can feel life returning, blood flowing back through my veins. We throw our arms around each other and dance with joy. Perhaps they will be followed by the Belgians, the Italians, the Norwegians, the Greeks, and then the Czechs, the Poles, Hungarians, Rumanians. The old continent can still do it! And then even the Federal Government will come crawling out of its bunker and join the European solidarity front.

The news drove the people of Taunusrodt out into the market square. The nightmare seemed to fade. Groups engaged in excited discussion, radios turned up loud. A few firework rockets were greeted with loud roars of delight. Everyone out of their houses and into the open. It seemed to be everyone's birthday.

Friends call up: 'Have you heard?' – 'What do you say about it?' People feel a need to have confirmation so that they don't feel they have been having some kind of a hallucination. That would be possible, after all.

Only later do I begin to doubt whether the Danish and Dutch initiatives can halt the unfolding tragedy.

Soviet troops have surrounded West Berlin. At least five divisions. The access roads and all other routes of communication have been cut. The three Western commandants have been ordered to surrender the city by midnight, or the Red Army will feel obliged to use force. The Politburo in Moscow justifies this dramatic and unprecedented step by claiming that there has been a blatant breach of the four-power agreement on the part of the Western allies: they have made illicit attempts to turn the city into a fortress. The Western garrisons have been secretly reinforced. They had even been bringing heavy weaponry into the city by rail and air. The imperialists were obviously planning to create an extra front behind the Warsaw Pact lines in case of conflict, to carry out 'military disruption projects'. In the present crisis situation, the Soviet Union and its allies could not ignore this threat. Warnings delivered through diplomatic channels had been unsuccessful; the three Western governments had simply ignored them. They now bore full responsibility for this intensification of the conflict, into which the government, Politburo and Central Committee of the Soviet Union saw itself forced after close consultation with its allies.

Why? Why this action after the courageous Danish and Dutch initiative? And again I have this sense that the military apparatus follows its own laws, laws divorced from all human decision making processes, and simply drags the politicians along with it. The politicians are just slaves, serving this apparatus. The computers have taken charge, and the members of the Politburo and the generals can only obey their commands. The computer has no fear, and nor can it be deterred.

Why has Moscow disowned the Dutch and Danish governments to this extent and ignored the political opportunity? Had the blow against West Berlin been so long in preparation that the Kremlin neither desired to nor was able to pull back from it? Has the army taken control in the USSR? Did the generals see the action of the Dutch and the Danes as no more than a thorn in their flesh? Or did it arouse mistrust in them? Are the Soviets looking for a decisive battle now?

Meaningless questions. We will fight to the end to avoid

113

accepting the inevitability of catastrophe.

The impotent protests of reason and the will to live.

11th August, evening

This afternoon I just couldn't go on. Total exhaustion. A nervous breakdown. My will to live has all been used up. Waiting like this is just defencelessness.

The three Western allies have categorically rejected any surrender by the garrisons of West Berlin. The Soviet demand is, they say, an unprecedented contravention of international law, for no state of war exists. Europe and West Berlin are still at peace. An emphatic warning to the Russians not to attack the city. The consequences would be unthinkable. The Western Allies could not accept such a brutal abrogation of their treaty rights.

My hand is trembling as I write. Something terrible could happen any moment. After a long chain of actions and failures, one second will decide our destiny.

The military machines on both sides are now in a state of the highest readiness. Aircraft ready for takeoff, tanks in formation and motorised columns all clear, their crews in position. Somewhere in the forests, missiles are probing the skies, their nuclear warheads in position and 'live'. The ICBMs are also ready. The firing keys have been inserted, the safety codes have been nullified. At this moment, nuclear-powered missile-carrying submarines will be heading for their launch positions.

On both sides, the radar technicians in their bomb-proof bunkers will be feeling sweat beading their foreheads. Satellite information is being evaluated and passed on by chalk-white experts. The officers in the operations rooms will be working away as if in a fever, their feelings a mixture of professional euphoria and human terror. The computers that calculate everything and give the orders cannot and must not be mistaken. The old men of the Moscow Politburo – long since installed in some bunker deep beneath the earth – stare helplessly at the advisers, officers and adjutants who hurry in and out, nod in response to all their suggestions, have no real understanding of the situation any more. The force of events and the 'experts' have the say now.

The equally overburdened president in the White House has also long since lost all perspective. He has just been loaded onto a Jumbo Jet complete with his staff. This airborne command centre will keep him in constant flight. The destruction of mankind is being prepared to perfection – by a few soulless machines.

On both sides, however, they are convinced that the enemy is planning his moves, and this war, in a cold and calculated way, that he is now deliberately going to the edge in full knowledge of the consequences. Neither side will recognise that the other might be acting out of fear, in error and because of false assumptions, dependent on the instructions of its computers.

A dicing with death by two élites who no longer know what to do and have reached the ends of their tethers. Deathwish. Death for Europe, for Germany.

And I am the chronicler of the apocalypse. It will be greater and more terrible than that of John and Dante's Inferno. It will be real, not some product of fantasy. The lust for sensation could be enough to drive back fear. A frontline reporter, who has no need to look to his own life any more. Keep observing and hold on. The end of mankind. An era that lasted millions of years ends in a few days. And I was there!

12th August, mid-day

This morning at six o'clock, the earth shook. Some dull explosions. The house trembled. My first thought: artillery fire, the Russians are coming. Sirens a short while later. The village is wrenched out of sleep. Screams from people as they run down into the shelters. To the east, the sun went up like a red ball of fire.

Nuclear bombs. My fear made me numb. I stared at Tina. She was holding onto her dressing table. Christina came downstairs, drowsy with sleep and asked: 'What's happening?' I heard myself say: 'Nuclear bombs'. The reality overwhelms me. I have thought about it, experienced my feelings about it, so often, and yet it still hits me like a fist in the gut. Nevertheless, everything seems so unreal, as if I was dreaming. Everything is so banal. Things seem to have distanced themselves, become very small, as if I were staring through a reversed telescope. My skin feels leathery, my eyelids are like lead. I can see all the bits and pieces of my life, as if in slow motion: childhood, my grandparents, the farm, mother and father, teacher, my boarding school, images and scenes are mixed up with each other, my running in a stadium, Tina in her wedding dress, Christine and Andreas as babies, friends, journeys, colours, fears, joys. Then I look into Tina's terror-filled eyes.

Nuclear weapons. Very close, all too present, merciless. The unthinkable and the inconceivable – how quickly and easily it has come.

The Soviet Union has attacked the Pershing and Cruise Missile sites in the Hunsrück and the Eifel, probably those in Swabia as well. After ten minutes, quiet as the grave. The sun has risen two finger breadths further and is very white.

The electricity supply has gone. The telephone is dead, the radio is silent, the television is finished. Isolation. Cut off from the world, no communication. Our world has shrunk to a tiny area. It reaches about as far as we can shout, walk, or travel by bicycle. Electromagnetic pulses? A deliberate attack on the power supply?

Battery-powered radios are still working. The BBC in London confirmed a massive Russian strike against American missile bases in the Federal Republic. The announcer was shouting, and speaking so quickly that he was scarcely comprehensible. This morning at four o'clock, fighting broke out on a broad front between Lübeck and Hof. Situation unclear. But the massive Soviet nuclear strike came shortly afterwards. All Europe on alert. 450 million human beings trembling for their lives.

The obviously distressed announcer then asked what would happen to England. Would Cruise Missiles be launched from there? What will the strategic submarines do? Will Great Britain also be subjected to a Soviet nuclear strike as a matter of course?

Three hours later, nine o'clock. The voice of the BBC

116

announcer, noticeably calmer, reports on the 'disaster' in the areas of the Hunsrück and the Swabian Alp affected by the Russian nuclear strike. The disaster is unimaginable. All he could do was talk about 'disaster'. A total of about fifty nuclear devices had exploded, so British aerial reconnaissance has ascertained. The countryside is just a sea of flame. After every other sentence there followed a bemused 'my God, my God'.

Tank battles are evidently in progress in the area bounded by Hanover, Fulda and Coburg. Elsewhere heavy artillery duels, raids by tactical bombers. Heavy fighting around Göttingen, unclear whether the city has fallen yet.

NATO Headquarters, the Federal Government and Washington are all blanketed in silence. How will the USA respond? Retaliatory strikes against Soviet missile sites in the GDR? Limited nuclear strikes against targets in the Soviet Union? What then?

At noon, the first communiqué issued by the Federal Government from its bunker in the Eifel. The Soviet action is condemned as an act of barbarism that fills the entire civilised world with loathing. There is talk of an inferno in the affected areas, but no indications of its extent. Everything will be done to give as much help as is possible under the circumstances. Then some minutes of messages and codes. The government spokesman's voice is trembling, he keeps stuttering, is so affected that he has to pause for quite long periods between sentences.

I feel feeble, alien in my own skin, but raging with anger and pain. I feel like I shall have to burst. The Soviet strike was predictable, it should have been part of our calculations. For years, we – myself and others – have been warning about the consequences of stationing American missiles in this country. We have protested, begged: the US strategy of 'decapitation' of the Soviet Union means suicide for the Federal Republic. The USA regarded even the stationing of a conventional Soviet regiment on Cuba as a threat to its security. The Soviets have been virtually forced into a devastating first strike against these strategic weapons, perhaps even against their will. Any normal person would have understood that. To psychotics, however, the notion that the enemy might also be afraid is impossible. Instead there was only pleasure and satisfaction when the

117

Soviets exhibited their anxiety. Fear can force the threatened person to attack, if he has the means to do so, and to remove the threat to himself if possible. The Soviets have always had the means, but an infantile Western defence policy has chosen to ignore the fact.

What happened to our 'teaming up with the strategic power of the USA'? What did the vaporised, incinerated, blasted human beings in the Eifel and the Swabian Alp get from that particular brand of teamwork? What good will it do us if the Americans now use their own strategic weapons?

12th August, evening

All the electrical appliances in the house are useless scrap metal.

This afternoon, Hofmann summoned everyone in the village to meet in the market square. Only a few came and ventured out of their cellars or the garden bunkers recommended by the German Self Protection Society. When they did, it was talk and talk, contact at all costs. For us the world is now Taunusrodt and only Taunusrodt. No one will help us; we have been thrown back completely on our own devices. The active authority of the Hessen state government – or even of the local rural district office – is no longer relevant. It exists only on paper. Mayor Hofmann showed energy and foresight. He had some important announcements to make, and he sent the village firemen, whom he had selected to be auxiliary policemen, into all the houses to fetch out the recalcitrant citizenry.

While we waited outside the town hall in the chill, two more bombers appeared overhead. They turned south with an ear-splitting roar and disappeared behind the high hills. Soviet Migs! The red stars on their wings were clearly visible, along with their pilots. 'They're heading for Biblis!' yelled Fritz Herterich, the garage owner. Terror. Everyone listened in silence, their eyes glued to the south. Ten minutes, a quarter of an hour. An eternity. I could feel my pulse hammering in my windpipe and found it almost impossible to swallow. As if in a trace, I noted that the breeze was blowing gently from the south-west. How often had Tina and I climbed onto the plateau

118

and enjoyed the view to Biblis and beyond on a clear day. The four cooling towers of the reactor rose white and shimmering on the horizon, like one of those fairytale castles in Southern Italy.

But nothing. No explosion. A dog barked, and a blackbird warbled on the ridge of the town hall roof.

These days we end up feeling pleased if the inevitable is delayed for just a moment. Why didn't the Soviet planes bomb Biblis? The whole of the Federal Republic north of the reactor would have slowly died in just the time it took for the wind to carry the fallout. All the result of two bombers. How did they manage to get this far in the first place? Where was our air defence system? Does it still exist? Our thoughts slowly turned back on themselves and churned over and over in horrified wonder.

Hofmann positioned himself on the town hall steps and shouted out that we should all realise that there would be no electricity for the foreseeable future. He did not know why. An enquiry by radio to the Local Government Bureau in Wiesbaden had established that things were no different in the city. It was possible that the electromagnetic pulse set up by the nuclear explosion had destroyed the delicate electronic components of the power stations and the grid system. The whole of Europe would have been faced with the same problem as we had here in Taunusrodt. It would probably turn out that most cars' electronic components had also been ruined. Only tractors and other heavy-duty vehicles would still be working. That was at least some help.

Whatever the case, solidarity was now the order of the day. Help had to be organised communally. No one was allowed to refuse service. The village had become a community where individual lives and destinies were all one. There was no prospect of help from outside. If we were to survive, provided nothing worse happened, then we could only do so by working together.

Hofmann is magnificent. A plain, simple man with a good understanding of his fellow human beings. Crusty and popular, proud of being a worker's son. Wants to retire next year, but would probably accept another term of office. He would be 73 then. At the moment he is indispensable.

119

Hofmann tells his villages that stoves, for instance, will need to be built. Old wood-burning and coal-fired stoves will have to be re-activated. Anyone who has a working stove of this kind should let others do their cooking on it too, especially families with small children. The old village baker's oven will be restored. Everyone will need help sooner or later, so let no one break ranks now.

Then there is the drinking water. It is only just trickling out of the taps in the houses. The electrical pumps at the waterworks are obviously broken. There are three wells with good drinking water within the boundaries of the village. He grins: and, of course, all the water will be free. Everyone should collect as much drinking water as their buckets, bowls, and sinks can take. The goods in the cold rooms of the village supermarket will be divided up. In the evening there will be a meeting of the villagers in the council house, to discuss the difficulties and how to overcome them. Everything is different now, though Hofmann hopes that this will be a temporary state of affairs.

Hofmann is stirring the villagers into action. Under normal circumstances the present situation would be seen as a catastrophe, but now it seems more like a local difficulty, for some of us almost a challenge. At least we have something to do and don't need to sit around passively, helplessly.

In the space of an hour we have been thrown back 120 years, to the time when there was no electricity. We shall have to relearn many basic skills – provided there is time for that. We have only elementary craftsmen's tools at our disposal, it is literally like being reclaimed by the past. Nevertheless, we are far better off than people in Wiesbaden or Mainz. If the power cut lasts much longer, the city people will be helpless. The authorities are simply not prepared for these situations.

Workshops and factories, transport and communications, hospitals! Nothing. How insane to even consider waging war with such fragile industrial societies. A few hours, just a very few nuclear weapons, and nothing works any more. 120 years of technological and industrial progress wiped off the face of history. Hunger, deprivation, misery, complete collapse. The 'calculated risk' of the defence policymakers. Infantile, naïve, shameful!

120

I am writing by candlelight. If only the end would come quickly. I feel numbed and cut off by my internal retreat from the reality of war. One long nightmare for two weeks now. Every nerve, every thought, is poised for the apocalypse. This crippling, energy-sapping fear! Each moment of the present hopeless, tormented. Have I ever lived any other way? Without this feeling of leaden heaviness in my limbs, without this trauma that goes on day and night, merging everything into one long agony? Was I happy once?

What is still keeping me alive? What will become of Tina, Christine, Andreas? Their destiny is also mine.

There is a full moon outside. Silvery-cold, indifferent, moving on its course across the sky. The constellations are dead. There is just this one planet, the one exception in the infinite desert of the universe, filled with life. There is no other. There is no-one to take our place. We should have looked after this earth, protected it, loved it, for all our resistance to life.

Instead it is being destroyed.

The Federal Government and NATO headquarters have imposed a total news blackout on the situation in the areas that have been subjected to nuclear attack – the Eifel, the Hunsrück, the Swabian Alp. They are obviously trying to prevent even more serious panic among the surviving population. But what do I mean by 'even more' in the face of this unending horror? Radioactive fallout could already be drifting over us. Am I already inhaling lethal chemicals as I sit here writing? Am I in the process of being killed?

The thought has surprisingly little effect on me. My feeling is more of a kind of defiance.

What has happened to the people in Ulm, Mutlangen, Schwäbisch Gmünd, Bitburg, Hermeskeil? The BBC newsreader this morning spoke of a 'landscape in flames'. The woods are dry as tinder and increase the destructive effect of the nuclear weapons. Sixty nuclear explosions, each more powerful than the bomb dropped on Hiroshima. Those areas of the country must be raging infernos. It is absolutely ludicrous to think of any kind of medical help. Some sixty beds are available throughout the entire Federal Republic for those hundreds of thousands of radiation victims. The thought makes me shiver. Hundreds of thousands of the most serious burns injuries! All the medical resources of this country put together couldn't begin to handle a hundredth of the problem. And it is not over yet. What a crime.

Did the Soviet missiles at least do a proper job of it? Is Ulm still standing? Schwäbisch Gmünd? Sixty nuclear warheads, planned area strikes, must mean complete extinction, the end of all life. But on the edge of the target zone, away from the Pershing sites! And everything so nearby. Despite this, I can't imagine the inferno that must be raging there. I can't conceive it no matter how I try. Just a sense of infinite horror.

Heavy fighting at the front. Göttingen has fallen, says the BBC, and Soviet armoured spearheads are approaching Hanover. Hamburg is also under threat. But the Soviet advance doesn't seem to be making real headway, despite a heavy artillery bombardment before the attack began. The kind of massive armoured breakthroughs that Western strategists had feared have not yet occurred. The British and the Americans have destroyed the bridges across the Oder and the Vistula with conventionally-armed missiles, NATO bombers have obviously brought the second wave of the Warsaw Pact advance to a standstill behind the lines. Heavy Soviet air raids against military targets in Turkey, though it seems that the situation on the Greek border is still quiet. Bulgaria and Rumania seem to be in no hurry. The position in Northern Norway is unclear. How much there is to say after just one day! But the conventional war is completely unimportant. One side will decide that things are going badly for it, then it will use tactical nuclear weapons, and then the war is over. Then the missile duel will begin.

If I live another ten days, that means I have another 200,000 breaths left to take.

13th August, mid-day

This morning I went up to the plateau on foot. From the observation point at the top I had a panoramic view over the

Hunsrück. The effect on the senses was beyond any previous imagining. A thick, black wall of smoke to the west, clearly still being fed by huge fires. The billowing clouds of smoke seemed to feed into each other, almost lazily. The black wall has disfigured the entire western horizon, as wide and as high as the eye can see. A terrible silence. The thick clouds like huge, sated snakes. There lies death's lair. It will come closer and spread itself like a burial cloth being lowered over a corpse.

Beneath me, Wiesbaden and Mainz are like petrified forests of humanity.

13th August, evening

Numbed resignation the entire day. There is nothing more to talk about. No more subjects for conversation. Everything is irrelevant except fear. The power cut continues. We are making do with an old spirit stove that belonged to my father. He brought it back from his prisoner-of-war time in England. I have not lost the art of working the thing without causing a fire or an explosion.

Mayor Hofmann is making house calls, inspecting the apartments. Radiates good humour, full of encouragement, advice, tips. 'We'll make it. Keep your chin up!' The man has become a giant. He has no intention of letting us either panic or subside into blank despair. Where does he get the strength?

Two suicides this morning. A pensioner and a farmer's wife. Acts of self-deliverance. In just a few days, life has become an intolerable burden.

The USA has delivered an ultimatum to the Soviet Union, demanding the immediate cessation of hostilities in Europe. Moscow has its own ultimatum demanding the immediate withdrawal of US forces from Cuba and, and, and . . . Ultimatum after ultimatum. Both sides know that the other will not accept their demands. Escalation is the only option left.

Soviet armoured spearheads have been halted outside Hanover and Hamburg. The BBC newsreader shouted: 'Victory!' A ghastly mistake. The real horror is yet to come. This war is just the prelude, it is what the politicians and the military leaders need to rid themselves of their scruples about using nuclear weapons. This is the moment of hesitation before the leap into the abyss, the letting-go into the unknown.

The Soviet advance in Pakistan and Iran has been halted with nuclear weapons, just when Russian tanks were approaching the coast. Words are not enough to express the reality of these events. All they can do – and that not adequately – is to communicate the fact, but not actually what is happening in Iran and Pakistan: soldiers, human beings, most of them young, incinerated and turned to ashes in the space of seconds, or with their skin hanging blackened from their bodies so that they look like skinned animals. Vaporised tanks, melted trucks, white-hot guns.

Fact: the Soviet advance has been halted. The rest of the 'fact': thousands of Iranians and Pakistanis will have been roasted and blown apart in this horrific way. Along with the soldiers, cities and landscapes will have been turned into lifeless deserts. For thousands of years to come.

It was criminal of the Soviets to invade those two countries. Might above right. But it was just as criminal for the Americans to halt the invasion with nuclear weapons. Might above right. Before they actually attack each other, the two big powers will bomb the weak, defenceless nations around their borders into ruins. Basically, they are protecting their own existences at the expense of the small nations. Incredibly hypocritical. If they survive, the sight of what they have done will be a terrible punishment in itself.

Even though the threat is coming closer by the hour, I intend to do everything within my power to prevent it from choking off the whole of the rest of my life like some clinging, poisonous mass. Tina says that she is trying to do the same thing, and sometimes she even succeeds. It is like a liberation.

The world we can see, touch, hear and feel has shrunk to within the confines of Taunusrodt. True, we could walk the twelve kilometres to Wiesbaden or Idstein. Nevertheless, it feels futile to have battery-powered radios and cling to them as our last connection with the outside world. To all practical purposes, that wider world exists only in our imaginations.

It is a fact that most cars have stopped working. Uncanny: an

124

invisible intangible force has quite simply paralysed them. The car stood for freedom, the conquest of distances, perhaps also for escape and safety. Now all we have left is the bicycle.

Only now is our absolute dependence on electricity becoming really apparent. We feel clumsy and helpless. My hand keeps reaching for the light switch. Now and again I lift the telephone receiver and listen to see if it is working. Will I ever hear Andreas's voice again, let alone see him?

The house martins have been the first birds to desert us. I miss those little black devils, the way they used to chase around the church tower of an evening.

14th August, mid-day

The nightmare did not end with the coming of day. We were awakened by screams of terror from the Thönnessens' house. Thönnessen hanged himself during the night. His son found him this morning in the cellar. Yesterday evening, his daughter came over from Liebichheim and told the family that she was expecting a child. That had been Thönnessen's fondest wish for a long time. He had already told us once that if his daughter and son-in-law didn't provide him with a grandchild soon he would adopt his own. What must have gone through that man's mind when he heard the news!

A Soviet breakthrough in the area of Coburg-Hof. Bamberg threatened. The BBC newsreader says this is not serious, the attack will soon be halted. Warsaw Pact troops are withdrawing from the Hanover area. NATO bombers are flying missions deep inside the GDR and Czechoslovakia. But Soviet aircraft also broke through the Western air defences yesterday and bombed supply depots. Conventionally-armed Soviet missiles have set two refineries at Wilhelmshaven and Bremen on fire. The effect of modern weapons is devastating. Heavy losses on both sides. Huge forest fires in the dried-out, wooded areas of Eastern Hessen and Lower Saxony. At no point is the population of these areas referred to. Where has it gone? *Quantité négligéable.*

Heavy naval battles around Spitzbergen as well as south of

125

Iceland and Greenland. The Soviets are obviously trying to break through into the Atlantic. In view of the nuclear weapons that both sides have at full readiness, these conflicts seem like preliminary skirmishes.

The most ominous news, however, from Saudi Arabia: the American units of the Rapid Intervention Group are said to have been as good as wiped out. The Soviets have better supply lines. American attempts to reinforce their troops from their bases in Oman and Somalia have failed. Many of the oil fields are in flames.

14th August, evening

Hofmann is 'commandeering' the supplies belonging to the supermarket and a number of speciality shops. If we are to feed the village, it has to be done in a planned way. In the course of his house calls, he came to the conclusion that the average household had enough provisions to last eight weeks. Then things could get tight. An admirable optimism – but it does us all good.

Strangely, no one thought of getting in enough candles and spirit lamps. They are impossible to get.

Frau Thönnessen has gone completely to pieces. Tina is looking after her. That life-loving man, to whom his family was everything. Fate is not only cruel, but cynical. As if it had not already pulled enough tricks.

Christine is very self-possessed. She refuses to stay glued to the radio and be shocked by the latest catastrophes. She is managing to read Marcel Proust's *Remembeance of Times Past*. She says she has no more expectations. Ralf, on the other hand, is noticeably more uneasy, is struggling with his fear like the rest of us. A chilling feeling, to be alive and as good as dead.

15th August

The earth shook again. The rumbling tore us from our sleep. This time it came from the East. Nuclear bombs. My skin

126

seemed to shrink and go icy-cold on my back. The individual explosions could be heard quite clearly. For hours.

We look eastwards from the terrace, where the sun is struggling to rise above the hills. After each explosion, a shudder runs through the landscape. The birch trees tremble. Shortly after seven, a black mushroom cloud to the north-east, clearly visible through binoculars. Shortly afterwards, several more rise simultaneously to the East. Nuclear bombs. Germany is sinking. Its history is coming to an end.

11.00: The BBC reports a widespread and massive exchange with tactical nuclear weapons along the front line. It is not clear who started it. In any case, it doesn't matter any more. Hundreds of weapons must have been used. A few of the explosions were so close that the Soviets must have been attacking military targets deep inside the Federal Republic, not just at the front. The mushroom cloud nearby to the north-east: Giessen? To the east, also really close: Büdingen?

12.30: An agitated BBC reporter, scarcely able to control his speech, tells of an inferno. Huge fires are raging in the combat zone, entire towns and villages no longer exist. The catastrophe is equally horrific in the GDR and Czechoslovakia. It is impossible to distinguish any more troop movements. British and American reconnaissance teams have not been able to find any signs of life at all in the vicinity of the affected targets. The extent of the horror can only be guessed at, because the resulting radioactivity is starting to fall as black rain and will also strike those areas not immediately affected.

14.00: The apocalypse has descended upon humanity on both sides of the front line. Both the BBC and the AFN report panic-stricken masses of refugees pouring away from the area. The fires are growing. Tens of thousands of refugees have been surrounded by the flames. Hundreds of communities are on fire. On the periphery of the combat zone, the roads are jammed. Retreating military units are shooting their way through to the rear, driving over the bodies of civilians. Like a huge hunting party.

According to estimates by the NATO High Command, some 2000 nuclear warheads were detonated on West German soil this morning. NATO used some 2800 – two thirds of which also exploded on West German territory.

Only now is it clear that the Soviets also attacked numerous targets in Western Lower Saxony, in the Palatinate and in Southern Bavaria with nuclear weapons, mostly hitting airfields and storage depots. There were several direct hits along the Stuttgart-Nuremburg autobahn, where French units had been moving forwards to the front. Massive devastation in the area of Ansbach and Eichstätt, where French *Hades* missile units carrying tactical nuclear warheads had been in position. The Western Palatinate also a raging inferno. Ramstein, Baumholder – wiped off the face of the earth. A direct hit on Kaiserslautern.

West Berlin in Soviet hands for two days now. No longer mentioned. A trifle.

16.00: NATO offers the Warsaw Pact a ceasefire. The Soviet Union is ready to accept provided that the USA evacuates all its bases in the Middle and Far East, keeps its intercontinental bomber fleet grounded and brings its missile-carrying submarines to the surface. Only then will some strategic parity have been established. The USSR declares itself ready to behave likewise.

17.00: The United States rejects the Soviet conditions.

18.00: The BBC reports that F-121 medium range bombers stationed in England launched hundreds of nuclear-armed rockets against targets in the GDR, Czechoslovakia and Poland. At the same time, several hundred cruise missiles were launched against Bulgaria, Hungary and Rumania by the Mediterranean Fleet.

Shortly afterwards, the BBC falls silent. An hour later, an unknown English-speaking station reports that numerous nuclear missiles have hit Central England. The missile bases at Greenham Common have been destroyed. At the same time, Moscow has warned the British government against using its strategic nuclear submarines, because if it does so the British Isles will be turned into a wasteland 'for all eternity'. The USA will be held jointly responsible for Britain's lack of response, since the Tridents cannot be fired without American agreement.

A sentimental thought that a scream must be going around the world, rising out of billions of throats from Washington to Moscow. What good would it do us? But perhaps it would help the others. So far only Europe has been annihilated, which leaves billions of human beings elsewhere awaiting their end. Can they prevent it? Stop this war machine? Too late.

I am very calm, feel almost weightless. My body has no feeling. As if I have opened up to eternity. The end suddenly seems familiar. I have lived through it so often in my imagination, suffered, died. Now it is enough. We shall await the end and be very relieved when it comes. What else is there to do?

I can hardly remember the entries I made in my diary this afternoon. Neither do I want to. This flickering candle will soon go out, and I shan't light another one for today.

The tragedy of youth. A crime on youth. I am sixty and have lived my life. Highs and lows, joy and pain, success and failure, desire and fulfilment. I have enjoyed life. The opposite of living is not death but failure to be born. Death is merely something beyond life. I have my past and my memories. But I must hold onto the memories that threaten to slip away from me. Not let myself be overwhelmed by the present. Save my life in the face of this fear.

How is it, though, for the children and the young, who have no memories, only the right to a future? That right has been taken from them with a kind of casual brutality. And those unborn generations!

Julien Green is right: we of the older generation are all equally responsible for this global atrocity. We put the destiny of the earth in the hands of intellectually and morally inadequate human beings. We did not defend ourselves when it was still possible. We allowed the Christian Democrat politicians Würzbach and Berger to say: 'One basic problem of nuclear defence policy is that Western society is no longer really prepared to sacrifice its life and well being if necessary to defend our freedom of national self-determination.'

It was prepared to do that. It has sacrificed its life. It has also made that decision on behalf of the children and the young

129

people, and has sacrificed their lives too. And it has no right to do that. That is why the older generation is an accomplice in a crime for which it can never – horrifyingly, never ever – make amends. This is total crime. Besides it, all the crimes committed in the history of humanity pale into insignificance. The young are only victims. We older people are both victims and perpetrators: suicide cases.

16th August, afternoon

Half of Wiesbaden has fled into the forests around the Neroberg. Insane, for the woods could catch fire at any time. A funeral pyre! It is only a matter of time until order breaks down completely and the masses come streaming aimlessly up into the Taunus. Children playing only serve to make the adults more nervous still. Mounted policemen are talking through megaphones, trying to persuade the people to go back to the city. In vain. Makeshift foxholes everywhere, tents, camp fires, expressionless faces, misery, waiting.

The town itself is like a city of the dead. Overflowing garbage. Vermin. Only a few people – mostly elderly. Fear in feverish eyes, no talking. Life ebbing from everyone and everything. Some ambulances, but without blue lights or sirens.

Nevertheless, the city authorities are showing astonishing discipline, a grim determination to stem the flood of hardships that is threatening to send the city under. Fear of total chaos. The city's officials are well aware, says Karasch, that the place would quickly descend into anarchy if they failed to give their all. There is an all-party coalition, crisis committees for communications, services, provisions, public safety. Citizens' militias have been formed from members of all parties to act as a support for the police. The trade unions, churches and other organisations are also active.

The level of radioactivity in the city has risen dramatically, Karasch says. Sixty rems today against ten rems yesterday. Radioactive fallout from the Hunsrück. The shroud is invisible.

Feverish activity to reverse the effects of the electromagnetic pulse, to have the city's power station back in operation. Coal

130

supplies are sufficient for two weeks. What then? Isn't long-term planning an absurdity at the moment?

All public services and means of food distribution have collapsed. The situation in the clinics is desperate. Some emergency generators not working. Intensive care units have been dissolved. Almost impossible to carry out operations any more.

They have been able to repair a few vehicles owned by the city, and so there is an emergency supply of drinking water. Nevertheless, the shortage of drinking water is extremely ominous. If the water supply doesn't start working again soon, they will be finished, says Karasch. The spectre of disease.

The first cases of looting. Aggression is on the increase, the struggle for survival rather than simple criminality. Citizens' militia active. Often robberies in broad daylight. Since the telephones and electrical security equipment no longer work, the police are powerless. The forces of order are constantly on call and are at the limits of their physical and psychological resources.

Danger of fires because of the primitive ovens and cooking equipment set up on open fires in people's homes, most of which have no fireplaces. Modern apartments are not designed for such extreme circumstances. One piece of carelessness, and the city will burn down. The fire brigade would be helpless. They couldn't even form chains of buckets as people did in the Middle Ages. 'We've just about reached the end,' says Karasch. 'With or without nuclear bombs. We can't adjust to a pre-industrial way of city life.' All social order will disintegrate. The city is simply not prepared for a situation such as this.

The population is being given iodine tablets as a protection against radioactive contamination. Dogs and cats are being rounded up and slaughtered. A precautionary measure aimed at avoiding the threat of epidemics. 'A massive wave of suicides' has been registered, but in a city of this size this is not enough to cause panic. Each suicide is a social problem solved. On the other hand, the countless drunks have become a severe social problem. Cases of drunkenness have become uncontrollable, as have the numbers of psychotic reactions. 'People are freaking out.' A private way of coping with the government-caused fear of death.

131

Calls for help from communities in the Hunsrück are being rejected out of hand. Emissaries come and beg for the city to send doctors, drugs, equipment, medical supplies. Hundreds of thousands, if not millions, must have been injured. But the city cannot even help itself, and besides that it has to be prepared for the worst. This morning there was a radio message from the Federal Government and at the same time a demand from the state government that all doctors and medical supplies that could be spared should be released according to the stipulations of the Maintenance of Health Law and sent to Eastern Hessen or the Hunsrück. The city fathers refused, arguing that they were now responsible only to the citizens of Wiesbaden. Doctors and medical personnel are being transferred to outer suburbs while they are not actually working in the city centre. Stores of medical supplies are also being moved to outlying districts. A precautionary measure in case of a nuclear attack. An attempt to learn from the experience of Hiroshima, where the bomb's impact destroyed virtually all emergency services at a stroke. But at that time, help was available from outside. Now no-one will be able to help.

Karasch and his colleagues are at the end of their strength. The collapse of a modern city. The entire country like a turtle turned on its back, helpless, even though it is still stacked to the limits with weapons and the enemy has been 'successfully' repulsed.

A laborious, perspiring walk back over the plateau. 'Fallout – Fallout'. Sixty rems even today. Once you have 250 rems in you, you start to die. And you increase your load with every breath you take, inexorably, mercilessly. Soon you'll have 250 rems. Just stop breathing! You can't. You can, because you must . . .

Shortly before the Plateau Hunting Lodge, a boy jumped out at me, maybe eleven years old. He was so frightened. Couldn't I take him with me? 'Where are your parents?' He gestured towards the woods. 'But you can't just run away!' But he was scared – and so were his parents, even more so. I, on the other hand, had to be unafraid. I was leaving the city, after all.

132

A catastrophe in the Mediterranean. Radio Bern: after all the vessels in the Soviet *Esquadra* had been sunk, Russian counter-attack with backfire bombs and missiles. A nuclear bomb dropped above the major part of the Sixth Fleet, including two aircraft carriers. Huge tidal waves have devastated the coasts of countries in the Eastern Mediterranean. The Nile Delta has disappeared, and entire coastal cities have been swept away by the sea.

More refugees in Taunusrodt. About twenty-five people, totally exhausted and scarred by their experiences. They sat down in the market square and waited apathetically. For a long time they wouldn't speak to anyone. Then one of the women said that they had been brought as far as Idstein by Bundeswehr soldiers. There they had been sent away again because the town was already overflowing with refugees. They came from near Büdingen. After the nuclear bombs fell, they had simply run away, kept going westwards. The woman could not find the words to express her terror. The noise of the explosion had deafened her. Then the fire had shot up into the heavens. It had rained red-hot ash. She had thought it was the end of the world. During her escape she had seen human beings stumbling around who had been blinded, and they kept screaming 'I can't see, I can't see!'. Everywhere masses of refugees, screaming and shouting! The soldiers had used the butts of their rifles to dislodge the fingers of civilians who were trying to hang on to their truck. The driver had simply stepped on the accelerator and kept going, or they would have just stayed stuck. People were even killing each other.

After Hofmann had given orders for them to be lodged in the gymnasium, it turned out that the group was made up of people who had never met before. They had been thrown together by chance during their escape.

Does this country still have any kind of a government? Is there still such a thing as a state in existence? The earth has swallowed up the government. No surrender. The war goes on, even though it has never been formally declared and therefore does not even exist under international law. Since early today, the

133

Americans have gone back to round-the-clock supply flights at Rhine-Main Airport. The airfield at Erbenheim is being used for fighters. Why no end to it? The Federal Government is obviously no longer master in its own house. The USA is in charge. The war goes on. I have a terrible premonition: the Americans are not flying medical supplies into Rhine-Main but more weapons. The interests of the USA will be defended to the last, and the Federal Republic has been selected as the battle-ground. Whose freedom are they defending? Whose national self-determination? Just forget it! This country has been wiped out for decades to come. Even those parts of Europe that have been left unscathed will not be able to help us. Millions would have to be evacuated. To where? Who would take us in? Who wants this shattered nation, even for free!

16th August, midnight

All that remains is a compulsive lust for destruction. It is no longer a question of defeating an enemy, just some deep-seated urge to bomb this planet to pieces. The heady joy of possessing instruments of total destruction, the power to unleash the apocalypse, has become real and actual. To be omnipotent for a few hours or days, to command the law of total action, to be God. The satisfaction of a child smashing a Christmas bauble with a hammer.

Kant's and Marx's assertion that the entire world must have been teleologically constructed to produce the final end of all creation: Mankind. What a mockery now. 'There is neither "spirit" not reason, nor thought, nor consciousness, nor soul, nor will, nor truth: All useless fictions.' The Twentieth Century has striven with all the power at its disposal to provide confirmation for Nietzsche's statement.

'It seems to me that nature's attempt to produce a thinking being here on earth has failed' (Max Born).

His work *The Destruction of Ethics by the Natural Sciences* remained unread, unappreciated. Never before or since has one man described the human dilemma with such merciless clarity and yet with such a fervent belief in reason. The natural sciences are an expression of the ability of the intellect to produce the most extraordinary achievements, and yet they are also at the mercy of political pressures, the claims of a destructive military caste, and of devaluation by economic interests. The highest level of creativity as a mere instrument of human destructiveness. Gallileo's hope that the burden of man's existence could be lightened proved doomed to disappointment in the end. It contributed to the destruction of the human race. Man's highest intellectual achievements outstripped his ethical powers. 'All attempts to adapt our ethical code to suit our situation in the age of high technology have failed.' Technological civilisation, doubly artificial, alienated and alienating, apparently omnipotent, has long since been incomprehensible and out of control, 'a process that was set in motion by reason, but is no longer within reason's control'. The natural scientists – slaves of power and profit – gave away control over their actions to sorcerers' apprentices; they had intellect, but almost certainly no practical reasoning, therefore no socially effective code of ethics. Born: 'Their political and moral judgments are often primitive and dangerous'. It is unthinkable to attempt to hold a society together without ethical principles, or to derive ethical principles from rational, scientific methods. 'The world is moving in the direction of hell at high speed, with a positive acceleration and perhaps even a rapid increase in that rate of accleration' (Robert Oppenheimer).

Those who warned us were dismissed as prophets of doom whose opinions were worthless: Born, Einstein, Oppenheimer, Sakharov, even military men such as Mountbatten, Pasti, La Rocque. They were not ambitious professional sectists, let-it-all-hang-out preachers, dreamy emotional adolescents such as are appearing in our cities now, but men who had deep wisdom, knowledge. Nevertheless, there were too few of them to outweigh the hundreds of thousands on the other side, those who surrendered their own ethical responsibility in favour of an ethic of political responsibility that contained no sense of obligation. This double alienation fed into a tendency towards self-extermination, and when that happened it would be final, as E.P. Thompson warned. No question of old-fashioned cultural pessimism, but figures and facts, and in the end concrete proof.

The lethal dialectic of humanity. Rilke's 'pure contradiction'.

What pressures – and what temptations – the politicians faced. It all began in the research stations and laboratories of the armaments industry, then continued in underground, air conditioned rooms, where strategic war in all its variations was simulated, and then went to the defence ministers and national security advisers of the heads of government. Anything that seemed makeable, was made. A total militarisation of domestic and foreign policy. Social conflicts became military problems. 160 wars in fifty years, twenty tons of high explosive for everyone in the world, cased in clever technology that thought for itself and could function under any circumstances.

'Exterminism' is the weapons system, and the entire economic scientific, political and ideological underpinning that supports this weapons system is that same social system that researched, selected, produced, guarded, justified, and keeps that weapons system at readiness – and now uses it.

And between these realities lay the failure of the institutions, of the judiciary, the political parties, the trade unions, the churches, the intelligentsia, the press. They constantly condemned: the destruction of the environment, nuclear weapons, the insanity of the arms race. They condemned the consequences! The men actually responsible were never condemned, or named. Those who had caused it all remained anonymous.

This was not by chance. It was an inexorable process.

Crazy dance of the shadows in the reflection of the flickering candle. Shapes reaching towards me. Hallucinations, a desire for the end to come.

Responsibility or determinism? Freedom and ethics or inexorable fate? Mankind as 'nature's highest purpose' or an unimportant structural defect? Kant or Nietzsche, guilt or tragedy? No answer.

Where did we get our trust in the capacity of this system to function indefinitely? Born echoes Nietzsche without knowing it: 'If the human race is not annihilated by a nuclear war, it will degenerate into a herd of dumb, foolish creatures under the tyrannical domination of dictators, who will rule with the aid of machines and electronic computers.'

We had already reached that stage.

The last hope of the sceptics was that we would learn from our disasters (Georg Picht). There were learning processes. Everything was being understood and described and therefore becoming predicable, controllable. But somehow those understandings were never translated into political decisions, nor did they become part of the collective wisdom. What did our policy-makers learn from the disasters of the Third World? Warnings of a 'threat', even though 120 million were already dying of hunger each year. What did they learn from the ecological catastrophe? How to breed poison-resistant, fast-growing trees. What about the disaster of human isolation and emotional deprivation? Cable television, forty channels. What did they come up with from the disaster of despair and drug addiction? To put people in prison and introduce strict controls. What did they learn from the 160 wars since 1945? Deterrence with 90,000 nuclear weapons and 45,000 megatons of high explosives.

An apathetic wait for the holocaust, whichever way you view it.

Christ, Kant, Marx: Utopias and progress on the path thereto. Except that the real objective was a planetary explosion. We lacked the million years or so necessary to balance ourselves out. The earth was a raw materials store, a factory, a garbage dump. Now a looted spaceship that is about to be scuttled. The 'will to nothingness'. That is the 'spirit of the world', the 'meaning of history', 'this lengthy weight and succession of damage, destruction, decline and overthrow . . . man, a petty, overburdened species who has his hour; his life on the earth is but a moment, an incident, an exception without consequence, something that remains without importance for the overall character of the world.'

Peace is the antithesis of humanity.

17th August, mid-day

This horror is tearing me apart. Fever, madness, hallucinations, iron rings around my temples as if my eyeballs were imploding. Damp with the sweat of fear, the fear of death. We are being

137

devoured, the apocalypse is reaching out towards us, merciless, inexorable. No escape. No help. No one can hear us.

Frankfurt has been annihilated. The city no longer exists. This morning shortly before seven o'clock, an all-consuming, blinding light that blocked out the light of the rising sun. Pale white, the inconceivable phenomenon of a double sun. Then – after an eternity – the noise of the explosion, as if the plateau had become a volcano. Spasm-like shrinking of the body. Deafness, paralysis, my back as if had been sprayed with nails. A huge fist shook up against the house and smashed in all the windows. Plaster fell off the ceiling. First conscious thought: a bolt of lightning. Second conscious thought: a bomb. A whistling, screeching sound in the air, then a long peal of thunder, the roar of a typhoon, Wiesbaden!

The sun went dark. To the east, a huge black pillar of smoke rose into the sky, flecked with red sparks. Fiery fountains shot out of it like carnival rockets. Red-hot showers of sparks rained down on the earth. The earth shook, as if it had been dealt huge blows, as if it was about to burst. The black, spiralling pillar seemed to bore its way into the heavens, and then slowly spread out to form a vast mushroom cap that covered the entire eastern horizon.

It was Frankfurt. The death of Frankfurt.

Hours passed, and then our senses returned. Shivering as if frozen. Tina chalk-white, her body shuddering against mine. Attempt to say a word. Futile. Painful awareness of helplessness. The all-destroying power of the moment, which hardly permits any feelings to exist any more.

17th August, evening

It was Tina's idea to climb up onto the plateau, while my dazed brain was still wondering how and where we could find a hole to crawl into. It seemed a monstrous thought to seek out the inferno instead. 'We have to see it,' Tina said. 'We have to face it.' Why? Where did she get her strength from?

A view of hell. Frankfurt was burning from the north to the south. Flames high as skyscrapers all joining together to make a

138

volcano. Black mountains of cloud in roaring, boiling mael-
stroms were bursting into the heavens, mingling, separating.
Great fountains of pulverised rubble, as if geysers were rising
where the city had been. Hissing and crackling in the air, the
moan of the dying city. Explosions, showers of sparks. A black
typhoon, endlessly rotating on its own vaporous axis, seemed to
swathe the entire city.

Further to the south, the sea of flame that had been the city
forest, growing all the time as we watched. The inferno seemed
to have no limits. The fuel stores at the airport exploded, the
planes, the munitions. A wall of flame rose into the dark sky.
Minutes later we felt the heat against our faces, the pressure
pushing down into our lungs. Then the Caltex refinery went
skyhigh. The jumble of pipes and buildings burst apart and
chased thousands of red tracers into the raging clouds of smoke.
On the periphery of the black cowl that had buried Frankfurt,
where Darmstadt would be to the south and Friedberg to the
north, grey showers of ash were falling in dense curtains.

Frankfurt, people, friends, life! Everything being incinerated, melting, vaporising, being torn apart. An interminably
long process of destruction. The inferno had acquired a life of its
own and seemed able to reproduce itself incessantly, with
inexhaustable energy and a moronic unconcern for the earth's
suffering.

Darkness over the flatlands of the Main, despite the high
noon-day sun. The smell of burning. Surrealistic madness. An
inconceivable atrocity, beyond human comprehension. Like
the Day of Judgment. I half-expect the heavens to open and a
huge, merciful hand to sweep away the bad dream.

The light from the fires was reflected in Tina's eyes. Her face
was free of sadness, her lips were constantly forming words.

Beneath us Wiesbaden clinging helplessly to the Neroburg.
Further to the south, Mainz and the Rhine valley. The glint of
the setting sun in some windows. The malevolent light of an
alien world. Or were we on another planet? What is still reality
and what is the dream? Are we dead already? Did we ever live?

In the late afternoon, thousands of people from Wiesbaden
with singed, tense faces bathed in sweat flood into Taunusrodt.
Their arrival in the defenceless village allows them to stop, look

anxiously around. Many continue their flight in the direction of
Limburg. The people of Taunusrodt feel violated. Aggressive
reactions, fisticuffs. Houses barricaded. Countless people from
Wiesbaden fleeing in the direction of the Wispertal and the
Rhine district. There are probably no police left any more.

Hofmann sends in uniformed members of the Volunteer Fire
Brigade. Using his megaphone, he directs the refugees from the
provincial capital to a meadow on the edge of the forest,
between two fishponds. The clear, energetic voice of Hofmann
penetrates their dumb despair. Someone to obey, a sense of
direction, of having a little path marked out and feeling oneself
taken by the hand. Instructions to the men to go back into the
city and fetch blankets and food. A strict ban on camp fires in
the wood. The firemen sort out rosters for watch.

The silent children with their huge, imploring eyes.

17th August, midnight

Frankfurt is still burning. Red glow to the East that reaches up
into the clouds, which seem to be alight themselves. Lack the
power to imagine what happened in Frankfurt. A kind of an
internal barrier for my own self-preservation.

After the sun had gone down, a Bundeswehr transport vehicle
arrived in front of the town hall. A dozen pitiful figures clam-
bered painfully down, stood around in bemusement, asked for
water. Hollow-cheeked faces grimy with sweat, filthy uniforms, knees shaking, boys of eighteen or twenty who looked
like old men. Drank slowly, looking straight past everyone. A
few lay down on the ground, propped up against the town hall
steps. A few people from Taunusrodt there out of curiosity and
Hofmann, as ever, on the spot.

A rangy, dark-haired Feldwebel gestured wearily at the
truck: 'Do somethin' for them in there, hey?' The soldiers didn't
move. Hofmann had eight bodies unloaded. Two dead, four
maimed until they were unrecognisable, their uniforms in rags,
hardly distinguishable from the blackened folds of skin hanging from the bodies. Two were obviously blind. Dr Casperski
was fetched. Nothing could be done. Badly inflamed and

140

suppurating burns. Irreparable dehydration. The men with eye injuries had radiation sickness as well. Too weak to stand. Vomit on their uniform tunics, their trousers filthy with diarrhoea. 'The nuclear explosion,' said the Feldwebel. Severe burns on the retina. Further diagnosis impossible, since his optical instruments don't work. Casperski shrugged his shoulders.

Several of the other soldiers also seemed affected by radiation sickness. They had thrown up the water soon after drinking. They calmly wiped their mouths and leaned back against the stone steps. They said nothing and did not react in any way to Casperski's questions. Only the Feldwebel, the driver and a short lieutenant seemed to be still intact.

The wounded were carried into the parsonage to Weigand. Casperski insisted that they all stay in one place, so as to be able to control their movements. The men seemed apathetic and let us do with them what we would. Their final powers of resistance had been broken. A deceptive sense of being home, being helped. Fell asleep immediately from sheer exhaustion. Casperski injected the burns cases with morphine. 'No one and nothing can help them any more. All they can do here is die.' Petzold offered the Feldwebel, the driver and the lieutenant the use of his house. His sons have not yet re-appeared. No one knows where they are. He also disappeared for four days. Not a soul in Taunusrodt has paid the slightest attention to the fact.

Still at Petzold's late in the evening. The Feldwebel comes from near Regensburg, had been attached to an armoured unit as a grenadier. He told us that his unit had waited for the attack from the East directly behind the B 276 highway, somewhere east of Fulda between Ehrenberg and Thaiden. The preceding days had already worn down their morale. Everywhere the local population fleeing in panic, some wandering about between the defensive positions. Their own increasing doubt, fear. The military columns had often got entangled with the refugees. Nervous officers had ordered them to press on ruthlessly because of fear of Soviet low-level air attack.

The German air force had been flying attack missions around the clock, to disrupt the enemy's buildup. They had seen hardly any Soviet aircraft. The automatic air defence systems would have hauled down any enemy aircraft straight out of the sky as soon as it got a fix on it.

Then, on Saturday, heavy drumfire, artillery and rocket-launchers, 'But our boys hit back good, y'know?' Then the T-72s pushed forward between the two villages. Behind them the Russian infantry, yelling 'Hurrah!' The Feldwebel believed that this had only been a feint attack, 'there was no real drive behind it, if y'know what I mean.' He couldn't say what things had been like elsewhere. The attack had been unable to develop, because the Bo-105 helicopters had been on the spot straight away and dealt with the leading Soviet tanks. 'Every one a winner.' Automatic anti-tank missiles, 'Them tanks stood no chance.' Their own Leopard tanks had not yet even intervened. They had still been rolling forward from their positions behind the lines.

But then, so fast they couldn't rightly understand what was happening, three very bright flashes above the Soviet positions. Neutron bombs! The Yanks must have lost their minds. Anyone who had been looking at the flashes was immediately blinded. Our own people! It was like the sun falling on your head. Then the mighty explosions, flames and smoke everywhere. One explosion at ground level had thrown an entire hill into the air, 'Right in front of our noses, eh? If anything, the bloody idiots waited far too long. But they didn't really need to use the things at all.' They had not been warned, they had not been prepared for a nuclear attack. The screams of the temporarily or permanently blinded. The nearness of the exploding neutron weapons, 'Which were only two kilometres or so when they went up, would you believe?' The neutrons went through you 'like a machine-gun through a chain-link fence'. The woods all around were dry as tinder and immediately burst into flames. The Russian tanks had suddenly started driving round and round in circles, as if the drivers were drunk. Some farther away had glowed red. The Soviet soldiers disappeared. A few dark smudges in the landscape, otherwise nothing.

All this happened within a few minutes. Once they had realised what was going on, the first of them began to run head over heels to the rear, and the rest were not far behind. They had paid no attention to the wounded. They were fleeing from the

142

effects of their own neutron bombs and the expected Russian nuclear attack.

What had happened to the villages of Ehrenberg and Thaiden? The Feldwebel: 'Just wiped out. Wiped right out. I never saw 'em no more.'

After half an hour, the Soviets responded with tactical nuclear weapons. The Feldwebel had trouble telling us what he had experienced. It was like the earth was breaking apart, he said. The air pressure had thrown him several metres through the air, even though he had been lucky: the nearest bomb had struck three kilometres to the north where the neighbouring battalion was stationed. Nevertheless, he had thought his end had come. He couldn't really remember anything, a total blackout. He had just run, without his rifle or his helmet, kept going westwards. Anything that took him away. Flames everywhere, things exploding and bursting. Three of them had come across the truck standing deserted on the road somewhere. They had picked up a few comrades on the way.

For hours none of them had been able to speak, and the truck had only been able to move forward at walking pace. Continual fear of further nuclear attacks. A mate of his had been suffering from the effects of shock. He had suddenly started firing at refugees from the moving truck. 'Someone took out a pistol and shot him down.' Another had suddenly jumped down and fallen on his knees, prayed by the side of the road.

The Feldwebel made every effort to give his report some shape, but it was impossible. Just fragments of experience. He kept constantly stroking his eyes. Always those countless refugees to drive through. A few kilometres from Giessen there had been two more nuclear strikes, very close to the city. They had turned south. Picked up the four men with burns. No idea where they came from.

The lieutenant, a thin, wiry lad, a reserve officer, about twenty-five, kept shaking his head as he spoke, as if he was about to stop. Long pauses between his sentences.

A grotesque situation: the inferno all around us, Frankfurt blown sky high today, we are a handful of survivors without a chance, and here we are hanging around in someone's living room listening to reports from the front.

143

The lieutenant said he knew that he had already collected a lethal dose. The symptoms of radiation sickness were unmistakable. As if he had caught a cold.

He had been with an anti-aircraft battery near the helicopter base at Fischbach, well camouflaged in a clearing in the forest ten kilometres behind the front. Their job: to protect the Bo-105, the best anti-tank weapon they had. They had been on full alert for three days, exhausted and their nerves in shreds. At last the fighting had started. Had registered the unexpected use of nuclear weapons with horror. Discipline had been maintained only with the utmost difficulty, three men had deserted. At mid-day on Saturday, the radar controller had leapt out of his vehicle and yelled: 'Take cover, lieutenant, there's something heading straight for us!' Before they could realise what was happening, a blinding flash, immediately followed by total blackness. The air pressure had paralysed every nerve in their bodies. The roar of the explosion had caused temporary deafness. The lieutenant had been convinced he was dead, he told us, and at the term he had acknowledged the fact with great satisfaction. Relief at how easy it was to die. He had come round again in some undergrowth amidst shattered pine trees. Fire all around him, a rain of hot ash and rubble. The burning air had made his lungs hurt, brought black rings before the eyes. He had no idea how he got out of there. The battery with its rockets at the ready had been blown away, a few dead comrades, peaceful and silent in the middle of the fire. Then he had run. You run automatically when there's danger. Four of them, the others half-dead, had managed to stop the truck and get a lift.

'Those guys were shitting on us all those years, really shitting!' the lieutenant said. The men on the General Staff and the defence experts must have known that it would come to nuclear war almost immediately. Above all, they must have known that it is impossible to fight in the middle of a nuclear war. 'I mean, it's just total, instant extinction. What can all those other weapons do against nuclear bombs? A few of the damned things, and the war's over.' Where there were direct hits, whole divisions must have been vaporised, pulverised, in the space of a few seconds.

Soldiers had become anachronistic leftovers from a bygone

age. Nuclear war was a matter of instant annihilation. The role of the soldier had been reduced to transportation, setting up, programming in the target – and then disengaging. All that was left to do after that was to sit and wait – on full alert – for extinction. Unfortunately this knowledge had come to the lieutenant too late. It was no longer of any use to him.

Nuclear war is not only the 'most terrible' of which man is capable, but its totality is irreversible. It will throw natural evolution on this planet back by hundreds of millions of years.

Dr Casperski came and said that the soldiers with burns wounds and two others suffering from radiation sickness were nearing the end. Weigand got up and went to them.

20th August, afternoon

Returned for the last time. Back home. We shall stay here. Our attempt at escape was a failure. The final rebellion, the final protest. Futile. Now that the decision has been made, I am quite calm. Tina as well. I feel a tug at my heart only when I look at Christine's young face. Ralf is dead.

On Tuesday, when the bomb exploded behind the plateau, where Mainz and Wiesbaden are, we leapt onto our bicycles and fled.

Or rather, we wanted to flee. In fact we lay there, incapable of moving. The flash of the explosion stabbed at our eyes like a rain of darts, the thunder threw us to the ground. The air pressure pushed in through the collapsing windows and hurled us together. The hill seemed to be collapsing. Deafness. Falling and falling into black depths. My sole thought: the end. Then the light faded and went out. Just the thunder rolling down the hillside like an endless avalanche. The very earth seemed to be exploding.

Christine was suffering from shock. Her screams brought me back to consciousness. She was standing with her hands over her ears, beating her head against the wall.

Behind the plateau, a fiery mushroom was rising into the sky, with storms raging within it. A flash of thought that immediately disappeared: over there, half a million human beings are

145

burning at this moment. Then I was alone with myself again.

Everything had already been prepared. We had intended to go via Limburg and Rennerod to the Sauerland. There might be a chance of survival there. Anything to get away from here, from this apathetic waiting, this humiliation, anything to avoid sitting huddled together here waiting for the bomb, like those rats that the villagers in the South of France stick under upturned buckets and then turn the dogs loose on. At least we could fight for what was left of life!

Now I know that I never really believed we had a chance, and that Tina never believed it at all. She just went along with us. She is braver than I. It was just a reflex.

Why did they pick on Wiesbaden? Because of the military airfield at Erbenheim? It was a two megaton bomb, at least. Two million tons of explosives, almost as much as they used during the entire Second World War! 50,000 railway waggons loaded with the stuff. A war machine that has got out of control. It just keeps raging until all life has been extinguished. Until it has destroyed itself. We simple human beings are no longer capable of that. This is global nuclear war.

Near Orlen and the Römerturm the shadow of the mushroom cloud overtook us. Behind us was a booming and crackling, as if the horsemen of the Apocalypse were approaching. We pressed on, our lungs almost bursting, racing against the black rain that would soon be falling. Just before the turning to Kirberg, Tina fell off her bicycle, suffering from complete exhaustion. She was bleeding – scratches that would normally have been harmless but could now be fatal. The radiation! My heart was aching with fear for her. I bandaged her up as if she had been seriously injured. She didn't want to go on. 'Only because of you,' she said. Many others were fleeing, as we were. A futile attempt, just like ours.

A few people on the street in Kirberg, staring anxiously south-wards towards the vast funeral pyre that had once been Wiesbaden. They seemed not to understand what was happening, just stood there gawping like children. The mushroom cloud had merged with the sky. It blanketed everything, east and west, like a huge black umbrella. At the base of it, the breadth of the city, constant sheet lightning. Hell seemed to be emerging from the crucible. And out of the sky fell Wiesbaden and Mainz, pounded to grey dust, returning back to their patches of earth. Dissolved into millions of tons of stuff. The clouds of smoke were moving lazily eastwards. The rain! Avoid being caught by the sticky, black rain . . .

We rested in Limburg, for Tina's sake. The town was like an ant-heap, filled with futile activity. Everyone looked the same, marked by fear, loss. Yet still living, still hoping.

We went to see Paul Kleemann, my friend. A protestant pastor, a rock-solid Christian human being. A desperate man, who when he was in the peace movement always had to fight against being drowned under the flood of disapproval from his superiors in the church and also the often slanderous fury of the local politicians. His strength was always his good Lutheran bible-stubbornness. A way with words which he used in ways that sorely offended the worthies. A man of God, toughened by his wanderings, who often faced the state attorney with some hard decisions. Always played skat with the workers in Limburg pubs, and had a never-ending store of jokes.

A broken man stood before us, hollow-cheeked, red-eyed, exhausted.

The one thing that gave him strength was the fact that his flock needed him. He was in church for almost twelve hours every day. He had become a last bastion for others, but where was his own God? 'I re-invent my God with every hour.'

Tina and Christina didn't want to go on. Only Ralf was willing. Christine seemed not to understand anything any more. Just kept shaking her head. She had had enough, she could do no more.

Tina had accepted her fate long since. I had not, and so I was in despair. At the same time, I was frightened of failing in Tina's eyes. But I had no intention of giving up, not yet. A drowning man keeps thrashing around until his arms are drained of strength and his thinking mind begins to empty.

Else, Kleemann's wife, was doing her work as always, tirelessly and without saying much. Again I felt the strength of a woman, and it irritated me. Why doesn't she show she is frightened of dying too? A rearguard battle in this sinking world?

That evening, Paul fetched a bottle of wine from the cellar

147

instead of water, for there was none. His emptiness and despair horrified me. But what could I say? To share the same destiny leaves only silence, for we can expect nothing of anyone else more than we already have. But then Paul said very directly: 'I believe in God. That's not the problem. But I don't understand him, with the best will in the world I can't. All I can do is hope that he knows what he is doing.'

The next day never came. We remained in artificial twilight. A fine, drizzle-like rain of ash fell without ceasing. The sky was grey-black. Such a solitude. Europe a huge Pompeii. The end of the world. So it was total nuclear war. Billions of tons of dust are starting to turn the earth into a black desert, a desert swathed in poisonous mists. I watched the burial cloth descending, with the invisible radiation woven into it like a curse.

An invasion began from the countryside surrounding the town. Within a few hours, Limburg was overflowing with deadly-pale, terrified humanity. Impossible to get anywhere in the old town. Refugees forcing their way into houses, banging on doors, shouting for mercy, holding their children up. The people of Limburg, overstrained and desperate themselves, defended themselves, refused aid. Ash on the children's heads like black snow, their eyes staring into chaos, the unspoken question that no one will answer. Life breaking apart in a thousand different ways.

Towards mid-day, the magistrate ordered the town to be cleared of refugees and for barriers to be set up. Police, fire brigade and citizens' militia erected roadblocks and barricades out of cars and building materials. The fight for survival was merciless. Desperate attempts at self-defence, fights, brawls, houses occupied. The townspeople helped to throw out the intruders. Nature's brutality, the amoral will to survive. There was no drinking water, nothing to make fires with, nothing. Limburg itself was not even a straw for a drowning man. But it was you or me, and so it had to be you. Women weeping, men cursing.

By around three in the afternoon, the town had been cleared. It was now like a besieged fortress.

I felt sick. I could hear Paul in his room, sobbing unashamedly. The double hell of a man who has to hold fast to his belief in God.

148

Townspeople who had managed to make their way in from outside and who had been let in by the guards, told of indescribable scenes. Out there, hell had broken loose. Millions of human beings had fled from the areas on the edge of the Ruhr District when the bombs fell there, heading for the Siegerland and the Sauerland. At the same time, a tide of refugees from the East. Villages and towns looted by starving mobs. Out there it was the law of the strongest, murder and violence. Deserters from the army were marauding around the area, taking all they needed at the point of a gun, especially water. Siegen, for instance, had gone up in flames after street battles between townspeople and refugees that had gone on for hours. Dillenburg and Wetzlar had suffered in a similar way, and Rennerod was just a heap of rubble. Vast forest fires because of the huge, unpoliceable numbers of refugees. Tens of thousands must have been burned alive. The blazing countryside was forcing the masses of people into the open plains. They will slaughter each other. The drifting clouds of smoke to the north were clearly visible from the top of Limburg's cathedral hill. The desperate masses will do to each other what the bombs failed to do.

This, then, is the 'defence of freedom'. Despair and futile violence. Not a hint of freedom, even as an idea. The slate is being wiped clean of such memories, history is ending. But the torment of this death, this loss of dignity, this cynicism! The desperate and the dying are killing each other. And in the process they are trampling on the last vestiges of humanity.

It is mid-day, and I have lit the candle. A pallid gloom. I keep checking myself, listening to my body, registering every sensation, even though I am deadly sad. When do the signs of radiation sickness become visible and tangible? The first bleeding beneath the skin? When you first vomit, your hair first falls out? Nothing yet. Just the ticking of the clock as time rushes by. Nevertheless, I have a feeling that I have got over the worst, like a man under torture when he is being dragged back to his cell.

Our nation produced so many to warn it. It played some evil games with them. Bertha von Suttner, the Liebknechts, August Bebel, Rosa Luxemburg, Georg Friedrich Nicolai (his *Biology of War!*), Tucholsky, Ossietzki, the many un-sung and

149

courageous ones, and then Albertz, Gollwitzer, Jungk, Sölle, Eppler, Mechtersheimer, Böll, Grass, the peace movement of the early Eighties, whose energy and imagination seemed inexhaustible. The resurgence of hope. The determination that life will still be preserved, that we do not need to give up mankind as nature's mistake. To rehabilitate Kant, resurrect Christ. The insecurity of those in power, the contest of reason with the lust for destruction. Finally the failure, the surrender, resignation in the face of humanity's inevitable will to self-immolation.

Tolstoy: all rulers are criminals. 'Those in power are often the worst, least significant, cruellest and most immoral people. And this fact is no accident.' Tolstoy expected nothing from those 'criminals'.

Against that, however, Nietzsche's hope: 'We have to reject in a very fundamental way the notion that the army is an instrument of self-defence. And thus a great day will come when a nation, tempered by wars and victories, distinguished by the highest level of military order and intelligence, accustomed to the most rigorous self-sacrifice in all these things, of its own free will calls out: 'We are breaking our sword!' – and shatters its entire military system to its very foundations. To make oneself defenceless, where one had been the power most capable of self-defence, out of a sheer pinnacle of feeling – that is the real way to peace, which must always be based on a peace of the spirit: while the so-called armed peace, which prevails in all countries at present, is an uneasiness of the spirit, which trusts neither itself nor its neighbour and half out of hate, half out of fear, will not lay down its weapons.'

In *Human, All Too Human*, he formulated the 'superhuman': 'Better to perish than to hate and inspire fear – this must become the highest maxim of every governed society.'

'As is well known, our liberal popular representatives lack the time to consider the nature of humanity: otherwise, they would know that all their efforts are in vain if they labour for a "gradual reduction of the military burden". The tree of war-and-glory can only be destroyed at one stroke, by a bolt of lightning: but, as you know, lightning bolts come from above!'

The bolt of lightning! The nature of humanity. Make oneself defenceless. Thomas Mann: moral and intellectual inadequacy.

Nietzsche, who pronounced God dead, actually wanted to save the Sermon on the Mount, and it was the Christian politicians he pronounced dead.

Tina said: 'We're going back,' I agreed. The situation was hopeless. At home, at least we could still see familiar things, books and photographs. Reminders of life. We were now existing in a different world. We needed to be able to cling to the past, to the time when we were human. Not give up our memories. The human ability to suffer is limitless. Perhaps that is the reason for this catastrophe: we never managed to set limits on inflicting or undergoing suffering.

The guards on the edge of Limburg were only too eager to let us out. We had only gone a few metres when we entered a world straight out of a painting by Hieronymus Bosch. These human beings were like deformed monsters, feverish eyes, faces distorted by panic, despair and hatred. Thousands were standing or camping out on the road to Wiesbaden, thousands in the fields, thousands in the forests. Hunger and thirst, especially thirst. All those people would never drink again. There was no more water. Everything was infected. The radiation had turned everything into poison.

Between the mass of wandering, standing, sprawled and dying human beings, men with stones, clubs and knives in their hands were searching like wolves for food and water. Soldiers among them with machine pistols and automatic rifles. Groups had formed circles to protect themselves. We were horrified. How long would it be before these desperate people started attacking each other? A mass slaughter would be unleashed. Some were still hoping for help to appear from somewhere. So they were holding on at any price; they were ready to do anything at all to stay alive. In the face of a catastrophe on this scale, there is only one rule: Survival.

Radioactive ash in our eyes and mouths, infected air in our lungs, panting with the exertion. But Taunusrodt was coming closer. Ralf, the strongest of us all, was riding way ahead. As we approached Hühnerkirche, five men jumped out of the wood and knocked him to the ground. He defended himself. One hit him over the head with a club, without hesitation. The men stood there in the road, waiting for the rest of us. We jumped off

151

our bicycles and plunged into the forest. They took our bikes and disappeared. We buried Ralf among the roots of a collapsed tree. Christine said nothing, just wiped the blood from his face and covered him with branches.

People are avoiding Taunusrodt. The nearby clouds of smoke over the still-burning city act as a deterrent. So we shall find our last peace in its shadow. Half the inhabitants have fled.

I note the end of my ability to make rational sense of things. My senses are overwhelmed, my level of perception is clearly deteriorating. Dream and reality are becoming one. A sense of tranquility. What a mercy to lose my reason now. What a mercy to die quickly. The pitiless necessity of living on.

21st August mid-day

The grotesque sight of the place where Mainz and Wiesbaden once were. I felt more astonishment at the completeness of the destruction than fear. I doubted my own eyes. A single, ashen-grey wasteland, a flattened, vast bed of dust, as if it had been levelled off by some huge roller. Here and there black smudges, still smoke, fire storms! Biebrich and the western parts of Mainz have disappeared under a lake. The bomb crater and the falling rubble dammed the Rhine. Biebrich hill looks as though it has been shaved bald, but below it, around the railway station and the writers' quarter, there are still a few houses, foreign bodies. The Neroberg is still burning. The dust clouds are moving eastwards.

The concrete framework of the Hessen Ministry of the Interior and the red sandstone structure of the main station allowed some sense of orientation in this desert. A flat, red heap of stones: the Marktkirche. Near it the city hall should have stood, with the state parliament building opposite. But there was nothing now. There are not even ruins, or even rubble, visible on top of the Gräselberg. Just a sheer cliff. The explosion polished it clean. Still a few houses in Klarenthal too. A black, smoking blob where Dotzheim should have been. A jumbled heap of concrete slabs: the municipal hospital complex in the Schelmengraben. Still a few blackened tree trunks in the

Kurpark, like sticks. In the eastern part of the city, at the foot of the hill that rose towards Bierstadt, some may have survived. There are even some structures clearly visible, well-preserved ruins, even a few houses that have been relatively lightly damaged. There might have been a chance for some people in The Aukammtal as well. But what do I mean by a 'chance' or 'survival'? The survivors will envy the dead. Those who were at the centre of impact are the lucky ones.

The sun was reflected in the artificial lake that had been formed by the Rhine. The field of dust sparkled, the evening shadows lent it a quality of plasticity. Total destruction, silence, peace. In order to destroy half of Hamburg in 1943, the Americans and the British mounted four raids. 3,000 bombers dropped 10,000 tons of high explosives. 35,000 dead in several days, an unimaginable inferno in the memories of those who survived. The trauma of their experiences still affected them years later.

Wiesbaden and Mainz were wiped off the planet in three seconds. 500,000 human beings killed immediately, the rest without a chance of survival. Two million tons of high explosives in a single missile, 200 times more than were dropped on Hamburg. What progress.

The burning forests surrounding Wiesbaden on its northern side have obviously prevented survivors from fleeing into the Taunus. To the west the fire storm of Dotzheim and Kohlheck, to the south the Rhine and the centre of impact, to the east the burning Kurpark and the dust that had once been Bierstadt. Wiesbaden was a trap. No escape possible. Perhaps still a few people alive in the folds of the undulating field of rubble, remnants of biologically functioning creatures in the Nerotal, the Taunusstrasse, in Aukamm, on the Dürerplatz.

21st August, evening

Pastor Weigand has made a crazy suggestion: we go down into Wiesbaden and try to help. Sentimental nonsense. How can we help? 'I am sure that a few have survived, and we have a duty to help them. At least we should be by their sides.' The stubbornness of a moralist – and too late. Help – grotesque, inappropriate, pure cynicism. The city is teeming with radiation, every stone is infected with death. But we need help ourselves. Who will help us? And perhaps help would still do us some good. Are we supposed to finish ourselves off? Weigand: 'We have been carrying death within us for a long time. Or are any of you still deceiving yourselves about that?' Those marked for death should help the dying. What an absurdity.

Weigand suggested that we sort out materials for use on burns and fractures from our own supplies. We could do without a lot of them now. Casperski could bring pain-relieving drugs with him. The firemen, who had been trained in first aid, could also come. After an hour, Casperski collects together a ridiculously small store of stuff. 'We have no more. We need the rest for ourselves.' Long hesitation by most of those asked to volunteer. The sight of what we were letting ourselves in for was deterrent enough. The radioactive city, the futility of the enterprise. But then also the sense that it was for our own sakes, too. To be able to do something, to salvage some remnant of meaning. Supplement the radiation within us, hasten the end.

Hofmann categorically refused to allow Casperski to go with the party. The doctor was still needed here, he had to outlive the rest of us. Otherwise, anyone was free to go down into Wiesbaden.

22nd August, midnight

We were there, we saw hell from the inside. Hell is not in the world beyond, it is on earth. The realm of the damned is here, is present, is reality.

It is impossible to describe my feelings. The sight of that horror numbs everything. Our energies diminish, the desire for a swift end becomes a longing. We have one last freedom: to drain the cup of sorrow to the full, for the last drop will be sweet. It is then that the torment ceases and a sense of peace comes. It is over, all lived through and borne, as much as was possible. I am no longer afraid. The worst is behind me. Death is just a release now.

The southern rim of the plateau was charred forest, and the

154

tarmac of the road had melted. The smell of burning. The plain of dust began just beyond the flattened North Cemetery. The first houses were still ruins, but after a while there were only piles of fine rubble. A round crater where the BP petrol station had been. A bestial stink. Corpses everywhere, flung out of their exploding homes by the intense air pressure. Black or violet-coloured bodies with cracked skins. The Platterstrasse. In a flat-topped pile of rubble, a bell. From the Maria-Hilf-Kirche. Everything had been levelled. A clear view right through to the 'inner city'. The concrete of the Coulin Bridge had withstood the blast. Down there the rubble was black, picked out with thin whisps of smoke.

To the left and down into the Nerotal, in the direction of the Taunusstrasse. There had to be survivors here. The first intact family homes, but the inhabitants were dead. Lacerated lungs. A few maimed by exploding window panes. Then the first survivor in an old-fashioned villa, a baby who might have been six months old, lying in the corner of a room near his upturned cradle. Hardly any reaction, dark patches under the skin on his wasted little body. Bleeding, radiation sickness. Children are the first to succumb to it. Helmut Geerts examined him. We had taken no drinking water with us. There was none in the house. We mixed a little mush from our spittle. The child brought it up again immediately, went into spasm, hopeless. He looked at us, not making a sound, just huge blue eyes. We were desperate, helpless. Our attempt to help in this hell had failed at the first hurdle, a tiny child. But even if he had taken nourishment, what then? What future would he have in a world that was in the process of dying, whose death was reflected in this child now?

Geerts injected a half ampoul of morphine into the child. It died immediately. We carefully laid it back in the cradle.

We went on. Fallen trees all over. The remains of roofs that had been blown away, houses with imploded doors and windows. A few of the inhabitants must have dragged themselves a few metres. We found most of them in their beds or in the cellars. A few of the villas with impact damage: gas leaks. Then another stop, another dilemna. A dead family in the cellar of a house, but a young woman cowering on the floor in a state of shock. Couldn't be spoken to. She had lost her reason. All our

155

attempts to make contact with her failed. Shaking her, hitting her, nothing worked. Glassy, empty eyes that were taking in nothing from the outside world. We decided to take her back with us. There was water in the house. We filled several bottles and took them with us.

In the Taunusstrasse, the first intact rows of houses, even though there was rubble and broken window panes here too. The survivors were like ghosts. Many already had radiation sickness with the typical symptoms: bleeding under the skin and in the eyes, hair loss, vomiting, diarrhaoea. Lying in their own excrement, suffering from high fever. But even those who had come through the inferno halfway intact physically and mentally showed little reaction to what was happening. These human beings had been gripped by apathy, not even conscious despair, and in a sense they were already dying.

The cynicism in the instructions issued by the disaster doctors and the Self-Protection Society about decontamination: change of clothes, cut the hair, take a shower. Really simple. In that kind of a state of shock, no one changes their clothes, and there is hardly any water.

Two men who were hanging around on the steps of the *Winston* restaurant stared at us uncomprehendingly and began to cry when they saw who we were. They still believed in help and salvation. They swayed up to us: 'Water!' Why hadn't they got out of here? A shrug of the shoulders. 'Why bother? Too late.' And where would they go? Left up the slope, in the direction of the Kapellenstrasse, there was only rubble, at the western end of the city was the blazing Neroberg, and to the east and south the flattened city. No way out.

Yes, they said, there were survivors here. Most had barricaded themselves in their homes. A lot of injured people had dragged themselves down from the Neroberg, screaming with pain, and they had looked so horrible that no one had been able to face them. They pointed to a few bodies on the street and in the doorways of houses. We moved closer: burned bodies, the skin torn off in black flaps, cracked lips, eyes that had burst, limbs shattered. 'We heard them screaming up there, day and night,' said the younger of the pair, himself little more than a wreck of a human being. But now, he said, there was quiet.

156

Geerts found four more in an alleyway, two of them in a coma. Their burns were already encrusted with swarms of flies. One head lifted wearily and stayed raised for a moment. Was it a man or a woman? The face was burned beyond all recognition. The other tried to crawl towards us. A gurgling moan, intolerable pain. 'Water, water!' We lifted the two cautiously onto the stretchers we had brought with us. Pain-relieving morphine. But hopeless cases. Geerts could not even remove the strips of rags around their bodies for fear of skinning them alive. The woman was making hand gestures – two of her fingers were still capable of movement – as if she was waving to someone behind us. Geerts bent over her. When he straightened up again, there were tears running down his cheeks. 'She says we should have pity and kill her,' he said dully. Horror, silence, a monstrous thought but a merciful one. Then George S. moved swiftly, took a knife out of his pocket, stepped calmly over to the dying woman and thrust the knife into her chest. He did the same with three others.

The strength seemed to drain from my body, as if someone had chopped off all sensation in my spine. I had to sit down for a moment. But I was glad that S. had found it in his heart to do what he had done. It was really the only way we could offer help: Euthanasia. 'We have no choice,' said Geerts.

Where were the doctors, the medical supplies that had been stored away in outlying districts with such care? Who had survived to provide a minimum of organisation? There was no one and nothing. The city was just a huge, desecrated cemetery, a ruined necropolis.

How many did we kill? On how many did we exercise our prerogative of mercy? I don't know, but in the end it was almost easy. So many of the victims were pathetically incapable of delivering themselves from their suffering.

The horror. Injured, sick, dying, apathetic, almost all of them marked by death. The stink. The terrible self-deception of those who were in the latent or transitional stages of radiation sickness. They believed that they were over the worst. But the level of radioactivity was still over 200 rems, and after the explosion it had been more than 500 rems, even in this area. There was no hope.

157

There was none for us either. We were carrying death within us, except that it was taking its time.

A near-ecstatic feeling, heady, enraptured. Sharp sensual impressions, precise awareness, complete unity with the self and yet also a kind of alienation from self. I heard myself speaking and saw myself acting – trickling water onto swollen lips, killing. Those ravaged bodies, relaxing at the instant of the thrust that killed. Their speechless gestures of gratitude.

The medical supplies we had brought with us were used up in no time. They were basically useless. We could have done with water and morphine, quick-acting poison or firearms. The only help possible was, when it came down to it, help with dying. Even people with less serious injuries begged us for this service, but that was beyond our power. To be permitted to die is now the only freedom that matters. No matter how many doctors had been there, that would have been all they could have done.

The many dead, the rotting corpses. Hundreds of thousands. Impossible to bury them or burn them. Epidemics and disease will finish off the rest.

23rd August, mid-day

In Taunusrodt too, the end is coming quickly. More and more people are giving up, descending into apathy, seeking salvation by taking their own lives. The limit of our capacity to absorb suffering has been passed, further existence has become meaningless torment. Body and soul are protesting against this impossible demand.

Our village has become an island of death. The only certain thing: the apocalypse is everywhere. The chances of survival in this once highly complex industrial country have been reduced to zero. Radiation sickness and epidemics will spread an all-embracing shroud over Europe.

The radio has fallen silent. This morning a hint of a voice, feeble and incomprehensible. Survival may be possible in parts of the southern hemisphere, perhaps in a few valleys in the Himalayas. But probably not. The nuclear inferno has shattered not only the industrial countries of the northern

158

hemisphere but has also ripped apart the synergetic mesh of nature. Billions of tons of radioactive dust have polluted the atmosphere, and they will come back to earth as lethal poison. The planet is a wasteland shrouded in poisonous mists. The experiment called mankind has failed.

The leaderships in Moscow and Washington very quickly let control of this war slip out of their hands. That was to be expected. We had known that. The total quality of the destructive power involved could not be controlled or corrected. Who started attacking cities? Why destroy the defenceless heart of Europe? Why a weapon of such terrible destructive power against Wiesbaden? Didn't the Soviets have other missiles at their disposal? Do Boston, New York, Detroit and San Francisco now look like Frankfurt? And in Kiev, Moscow, Leningrad, Leipzig, Gdansk, Budapest, Prague, is it like Wiesbaden?

Pointless to ask. If only half the nuclear weapons in existence have been used, they will total 20,000 megatons. Half of that would have been enough for this planet. A few days to destroy what took billions of years to evolve. Fantastic! The fragile, complex systems of nature were not attuned to handling the problem of mankind.

Now that I am quite calm and have made my peace with myself, because I am no longer tormented by the will to live and am sure of my final freedom, my senses can begin to encompass this global drama in its insane magnitude, its monstrousness and totality. Even the banality of its possible cause has a powerful effect. I can imagine that this apocalypse could have been unleashed by a very minor foul up. Say, for instance, the commander of a Pershing site had lost his nerve. After the Americans and Russians had started to shoot at each in the Middle and Far East, the safety codes were lifted. The particular commander, however, maybe a thirty-five-year-old major, knew that he and his four Pershings were right at the top of the Soviet's list of targets. The targeting computer of a Soviet nuclear missile was programmed to head straight for the major's site, and it could be launched at any time. The site commander on the other side also had his finger on the button. The American major also knew that the Soviets had at all costs to stop him from launching his missiles, because for them it was a question of life or death. He and his Pershings were a threat to their existence. But he only remained a threat, and therefore a high-priority target, for as long as he had not launched his missiles. If he were to launch his Pershings, he would no longer be a target for the Soviets, and then the Soviet commander would have to re-programme his missile, probably an SS-22, and point it at another target. He and his men would be saved. That was his chance: to fire first. Because this major was only human, was incredibly scared, despite many years of training, despite thorough tests of his qualifications. He was not too intelligent, he had no particularly strong moral scruples, he was used to obeying orders without much thought, he felt himself to be part of this system. And nevertheless he was having feelings that were growing stronger now that he knew he was a target for the enemy. He had a wife and child in a small town near Kansas City. To wait meant suicide. But he had no intention of committing suicide, of being sacrificed. His fear allowed him to become fully aware of the absurdity of the system, the machine in which he was a tiny cog.

So he tore open the folder containing the final code, in total panic, did not wait for his Corps Commander's order. He launched the four Pershings. Perhaps his crew mutinied and forced him to do it, perhaps they fired the missiles off themselves.

When the four missiles appeared on the Russian's radar screens, the launch order was automatically given. Fifty SS-22s raced into the sky in the space of three minutes, in an attempt to prevent the launch of the rest of the Pershings and Cruise Missiles. Now, of course, the Soviets believed that they were faced with a planned attack, they supposed that the Americans had now decided on a decisive blow, the 'selective strategic war'. The possibility that a site commander had lost his nerve was one which they did not consider.

So at the same time, four ICBMs started out towards the USA. In retaliation.

In the strategic command post in Omaha, they had hardly managed to register the young major's foul up. The Americans had never taken into consideration the fact that there is hardly anything more natural than a human being losing his nerve.

While the High Command was still evaluating the reports, trying to reach the Corps Commander in his bunker in Britain and providing a report for the president, the computers signalled maximum emergency: Soviet ICBMs approaching.

Without any knowledge of the circumstances – eleven minutes have passed since the foul up with the Pershings – the Americans believe that the Russians are carrying out a full-scale nuclear attack. The riddle of why the Soviets are sending only four missiles is insoluble under these conditions. The worst possible case is immediately assumed: a massive Soviet attack against the stilos containing the Americans' ICBMs. Surely the computers have only managed to pick up four Soviet missiles out of 600 or 700. Can happen. There are still twenty-five minutes left in which to correct the mistake. But their conviction that they are dealing with a computer underestimate is unshakeable, because selective nuclear strikes are not considered part of Soviet strategy, are not among the prepared options. In the command post in Omaha, they are solidly convinced that the Soviets have launched a massive attack. After ten minutes, the president's 'fire at will' order is received, the ICBMs are ready for launching with their target computers programmed for new objectives, since it would be pointless to hit the (probably) empty Soviet missile bases. The Midgetmen and MX missiles will destroy cities and industrial centres. They start after twenty minutes. Strategic bombers carrying 8,000 Cruise Missiles are already in the air, heading towards the borders of the Soviet Union.

After another ten minutes, only four Soviet missiles actually arrive. The members of the General Staff in their bunker in Omaha register the fact with amazement and then with despair. It is too late. The war machine is running. Nothing and no one can stop it now.

Meanwhile, the Soviets have got a fix on the 500 approaching American missiles. They are feverishly preparing their own missiles for launching, for they suspect that the strike is aimed at their strategic weapons. The Soviet missiles now have to be reprogrammed too, since a strike against the empty American silos would be futile. 1700 missiles bearing the red star shoot into the sky, each carrying ten to fifteen warheads, each warhead with ten times the explosive power of the bomb that fell on Hiroshima.

The two superpowers are buried under ash and rubble – after they have destroyed Europe. But both still have their strategic submarines with more than double the destructive power already unleashed. Missile after missile climbs out of the world's seas.

Now the blue planet is being destroyed, totally and finally.

Was that how it was? It could have been so. No one will ever know the answer. It is possible, too, that it was a Soviet commander who lost his nerve, perhaps even the Soviet military leadership. Perhaps they struck first against the Pershing sites, which the Americans interpreted as a signal that the enemy was prepared to go to the limit. Even though the Americans had originally not intended to die for Europe under any circumstances, they now saw themselves forced to go for their last chance, however vague and dangerous it might be: they began a massive surprise attack on the Soviet Union. But the Soviets had long been prepared for it, and their missiles were ready to go. When the enemy missiles appeared on their radar screens, they let fly. According to their plan, things should have happened differently. The plan foresaw bringing the enemy to his senses with one, well-aimed strike. The plan failed because it did not take account of human beings.

In any case, the destiny of the planet hung on the slender thread of one or just a few men's nerves. And it has been so for decades, day and night. The sword of Damocles hanging over the planet.

If one day in the far future extra-terrestrial beings should land on earth, they will puzzle over the causes of this catastrophe, just as we speculated on the extinction of the dinosaurs. They will assume it was a natural disaster or some terrible plague. They will regret being unable to meet any living representatives of this race. They will dig among those ruins that are still visible, will try to reconstruct the story of how this catastrophe occurred many thousands of years before. It will never occur to them that this highly intelligent race could have exterminated itself. Because we must have been a highly intelligent race, as the traces left behind show clearly.

On the other hand, the laws of nature apply even in the Cosmos. There is no place for intelligence in the universe, which is unconscious and functions on its gigantic scale according to physical laws. Wherever intelligence evolves, it obviously carries within it the urge to self-destruction. Before, therefore, these extraterrestrials could have developed the technological capacity to make contact with other planets or even land on them, they would have created weapons of mass destruction and wiped themselves out. As we are doing now. In its highest level of perfection – in the development of consciousness and intelligence – evolution has been at its most imperfect. Consciousness was not sufficiently firmly anchored in the life force, it did not liberate mankind but bind it. Thus all we were left with was the idea, the experiment, the first draft.

23rd August, evening

Now all the children are dying, quickly and quietly. A short phase of vomiting; fever, diarrhoea, inflammation of the throat, bleeding, weight loss – then it is over. It is like a mass escape. An indictment, the only way left for those children. Just out of the world as quickly as possible, let those adults get on with it. Include us out. Lessing dubbed his son, who had hardly been born when he upped and left again after just a few hours, 'the wise one'. The children's deaths don't increase the sufferings of their apathetic parents; they just deepen the emptiness. In a sense their deaths are even merciful. They ease their parents' burden.

The old and the sick are following the children's example. The firemen trundle their handcarts round every day. They have fetched at least one dead person from each house now – Hofmann has had a big grave dug. We shall all lie side by side in a kind of harmony. Wiegand has his work cut out, while Dr Casperski's skills have become almost superfluous.

Though we won't admit it to each other, Tina and I are watching each other with a painful intensity. I can sense her eyes probing for the first symptoms in me every morning, every hour. Christine too. For my part, I secretly check to see if Tina

163

has been vomiting. When I stroke her forehead, I feel if she has a temperature. She looks really miserable, exhausted. Nevertheless, she has not deserted me – yet. Christine has made an astonishing recovery. But what does it matter? Radiation sickness is capricious. We are all aware that our long farewell process began long ago. We know that we are only living on borrowed time. We each sense the closeness of the other as we do our own aliveness, the breath and heartbeat of each other is our own. Infinite love for each other. This is how we will win our race against time.

Hofmann was just here and told me that the farmers' livestock is dying in droves, in the fields and in its shed. Contaminated grass. Since this morning the bulldozer has been gouging out deep trenches all around the village. The tractors have been pushing the carcases into them. But how do you get rid of a thousand cattle, plus as many pigs, hens, geese, ducks? Nevertheless, it has to be done. If they were left, the epidemic risk would be disastrous within a couple of days.

The thought of dying from the plague arouses a degree of defiance. A few men decide to go to the neighbouring villages and try to co-ordinate action. It will go on from there. We know that it is hopeless. The importance of the attempt lies in the act itself: to do something, simply to be doing something, even if it is ridiculously ineffectual. Stubborn resistance, that is the importance of all this.

In the forests, the wildlife is dying too. Yesterday already the first sick deer emerged out of the woods and into the clearings. They are more vulnerable than human beings. Not a single bird in the gloomy-grey sky. Masses of dead doves are being collected up in the streets around the church tower and the market square. Dead birds in the garden. They are falling literally out of the trees. Tits, blackbirds, sparrows, robins.

How quickly and consistently everything happens. According to a cruel law. It knows no miracles and allows no hope.

24th August, mid-day

A robbery this morning. Farmer Brandt, who was collecting dead livestock together with a few other men, alerted Hofmann. Six soldiers were approaching the village, all armed with machine pistols, obviously capable of anything. We saw them coming down from the Orlen hill in the pale twilight. Hofmann had weapons distributed, then we went out to meet them, four of us. The men demanded water and food. One pointed to the tractor: 'That too!' They had their machine pistols trained on us. Petzold said with great presence of mind that we had only poisoned water, the food was ruined, because after all the bomb had gone off right behind the hill. We were only just alive ourselves. But they could take what they liked. They were welcome. Also, there was an epidemic raging here. Petzold indicated the pit and the bloated carcases. No chances here for anyone who wanted to survive.

The soldiers stared at us. Then one yelled 'Boys, let's get out of here!' They ran off. After they had gone about twenty metres, one turned, slipped the safety-catch on his machine pistol as he back-pedalled, and fired. Petzold was killed on the spot.

24th August, evening

Dr Caperski has reached the end of his strength. Hofmann has ordered him to take a good rest, but the doctor knows what is going on. So do we. Today alone we buried thirty-six in the mass grave. Lime on the bodies and a handful of earth. The grave will have to do for many more yet. No sounds of grief from the houses. Just silent despair that is starting to give way to a kind of serenity. Our senses are becoming blunted. We simply can't take it in any more. Job would never change places with us. We can't put our hopes in the Lord's lifting these plagues from us if we do penance.

Our 'disaster committee' at Mayor Hofmann's house is keeping just one aim in mind: the resources and potential of the village should be concentrated in such a way that we can give a chance of survival, if such is at all possible, for the strongest of us. We don't yet know who that might be, perhaps a few young people in their twenties. We start from the premise that a few may have a chance of survival and include the assumption, vague hope though it is, that help may still come from outside. 'Iron rations' of food and water are being stored at the town hall for this purpose. Plus drugs, tools, and three battery-powered radios with spare batteries. The forestry office has supplied five rifles, the police station six machine pistols and several pistols. Spare parts are being collected for the two tractors and the bulldozer. Chief causes of damage and repair procedures are being described as thoroughly as possible in writing, in terms that even laymen can understand and act upon if necessary.

The most difficult problem is the establishing of an organisational and administrative system for the village. Hofmann, whose ravaged appearance is causing us all great concern, has named as his successor Campen, the young headmaster of our school, who after the death of his two children has been literally death-defying in his capacity for action. Campen will then name a successor himself, should he be taken from us.

The same system is to apply to the selection and replacement of members of the five-strong security unit, whose task – having been supplied with arms – will be to ensure a minimum degree of order and 'protection from external danger', to increase the survival chances of those who may still be able to make it.

24th August, midnight

The days drag by in gloomy twilight. When I read my diary entries, I realise how meaningless it is to attempt a chronology. If it were not for my concern about Christine and Tina, I would be quite capable of viewing this global catastrophe as no more than an infernal drama. My senses are extremely sharp, they register every detail. I have known the script for a long time, I know which scene follows which, and I know how it ends. The script ought to be known to everyone, for it took years to write. It has had many authors since 1945: American presidents and defence secretaries, senators, defence policymakers and military men, Soviet general secretaries, Politburo members and marshals, German Federal Chancellors, defence and foreign ministers, party leaders, parliamentary deputies, scientists, manufacturers, managers, officers. They may have written the script with the aim and the hope that it would never have to be staged. But very early on they overlooked the fact that the script

166

had become a thing with a life of its own. It had encompassed everyone's thinking, planning and action, had welded together huge apparatuses into a functioning system, and finally had subjected the most powerful industrial countries to its will, including their scientific, technological, intellectual, organisational, communicative, and planning capabilities. By the end, the 'authors' of the script were no more than actors in the drama. For scene after scene, it carried on writing itself and giving them their roles. The men who were supposed to be the writers and directors became actors who knew their roles only too well. They became victims of their own script. And all the while they were still fancying themselves as authors, who would manage a 'happy end' in the last act.

Total theatre: Not just the stage but the entire building is blown to bits.

In the long run, it was impossible to live with that contradiction.

Good and evil, truth and lie, honesty and slyness, freedom and oppression, sympathy and harshness, wisdom and stupidity, maturity and infantility, hope and despair, reason and fanaticism, greed and generosity, love and hate – the deadly contradiction in each of us. Nature has not given itself or us the time to reconcile that contradiction.

Franz-Josef Strauss once dubbed Europe, bristling as it was with weaponry, 'the safest place in the world'. President Reagan called his nuclear missiles 'peacekeepers'. In the end, the pastor was right: 'Either we abolish armaments – or they will abolish us.'

There was an old grandfather clock in my grandparents' living room. If we stopped the pendulum, the mechanism would tick on for a few more strokes with a shrill, grating sound. It went right through us, because grandmother once scolded us with the words: 'No one can stop time, only God can do that. And that is why he has sent death . . .' Now humanity has stopped the pendulum of the world's clock.

167

25th August, mid-day

Dr Casperski, that fine, sensitive man, has killed himself. And what use was there in his staying here? Death everywhere, nothing to be saved or helped. He had become superfluous. And he had prepared so thoroughly for just such a catastrophe as this, honestly convinced that doctors were needed particularly urgently in times of disaster. And even if only a few lives could be saved – the doctor could never refuse to help. The catastrophe came, and he could not save a single life. All he could do was help people to die, like any other feeling person. For this last duty, however, we do not need a medical training. Now the only person he has been able to help is himself.

Our strength is fading. The smell of decay makes it hard to breathe. In the houses of Taunusrodt there are corpses, and no one is fetching them. Neither can we get rid of the animal carcases. The 'post-nuclear' consequences are reaching their peak. The white spruce in the garden have turned brown, the birches yellow, and the beech trees' leaves are curling in on themselves. The roses and the dahlias are withered and weedy. The dew these past cool nights has turned the fallen dust into a dark-brown radioactive film that covers everything. Once the vegetation has gone, we will lose the last theoretical basis for our existence. When the black blanket of dust disperses and the sun breaks through, the dead forests will ignite, or perhaps the last human beings camping out there will light their own funeral pyre.

25th August, afternoon

We made ourselves some tea on my father's old spirit stove. The stove and the tea awaken long-buried memories.

Father used this stove to brew teas he picked himself – coltsfoot, lime-blossom, yarrow. When too much spirit had gone into the bowl, there was always a threat of an explosion. Father would mock myself and my brother at such times because we would station ourselves by the door, ready to save the house in case it blew up.

Tina found father's tea-making habits priceless. The first time she saw him messing with the spirit stove, she laughed so much that tears ran down her cheeks. My father, deadpan as ever, was poking hastily at the apparatus with the tips of his fingers, attempting to get it under control. His tie was threatening to catch fire. He would have needed three hands.

Tina looks terrible, pale, with red-rimmed eyes, exhausted. I found a few tufts of hair in the bath this morning. The awful certainty took my breath away. Perhaps she is just exhausted and overstressed! I struggle to convince myself.

26th August, morning

Tina is sick, it can no longer be denied. She was forced to vomit several times during the night. The first subcutical bleeding on the upper part of her body. High temperature, chill, bleeding gums. The 'hematopoitic syndrome'. Radiation sickness. I shall die with her. Christine is with her now.

26th August, mid-day

Taunusrodt is dying out. There are no more children, old people. The earth is emptying. Sellout. A mass dying like in the Middle Ages when the plague was raging. Smallpox, malaria and hepatitis are becoming more and more common, as are typhus, paratyphus, yellow fever, diptheria. Trillions upon trillions of bacilli are rising from the unburied corpses and carcases and spreading with all the speed of poisoned gas. Now comes the 'biological weapon'. Midges and flies are clinging to our windows in seething black bunches that match the black plastic we have hung over the gaping holes. We have moved Tina down into the cellar. We have stopped the window with pieces of bed linen so that the flies and midges can't bother her.

Mayor Hofmann is dead.

A few young people are keeping to the 'catastrophe system'. They have set up barricades on the roads to Limburg and Idstein, to stop anyone who might be dragging themselves towards the village. The new arrivals, already marked by death and totally exhausted, stop in front of them, lie down on the ground and simply don't get up again. This is the village's only defence. Only a few make their way around the barricade and come into the village. Then there they are. They don't disturb anyone. There is plenty of room.

Getting rid of the bodies is the biggest problem. The two tractors are at work incessantly. The young people work with grim determination, fighting for their chance. Christine is also involved. Better to fight for her life than to give up.

Prepared a light soup for Tina on the spirit stove. She kept it down. A glimmer of hope? No.

The end will be a release. Living is too brutal, a slow execution.

Earlier, I firmly decided that if it came to this I would think of what a great privilege it is to have lived. Life has been worth the price of death. Is that still true? This helplessness, this loss of dignity, this brutality. The only thing that matters now is these last hours with Tina.

27th August, mid-day

The black blanket has dissolved. The sun has returned at last. But it sits up there in the sky like a razor-sharp, yellow sliver of glass. A blinding, destroying light. I had difficulty holding Christine back from going outside. No one can go outside now, for it means instant blindness and a swift death.

The sun's ultraviolet light is streaming straight down towards the earth without any filter. The nuclear explosions destroyed the ozone layers in the stratosphere. A further indication that there must have been a global nuclear war. One of those 'post-nuclear consequences'! This unearthly light has a kind of oppressive fascination, strips me of all sense of reality. Like in a science fiction film.

Wrapped up in plastic foil and sheets, my glasses tinted black and stuck to my head, an apparition, I went through the village calling out: 'Don't go out in the sun! Deadly dangerous! Radiation! Wrap yourselves up! Protective clothing! Stay in your homes! Don't go out, blindness! Deadly danger!'

170

Life has shrunk to a few square metres and a few hours. Now even the sun is a killer. The thing that was once the source of all life is burning up the last remnants of existence on the earth. We have turned the sun into a monster. But it will continue in its course, even if it shines on a dead planet.

27th August, afternoon

Gentle scrabbling noises against the plastic foil covering the window, as if someone was pushing lightly against it. Blinded insects. The ultraviolet radiation has burned out their eyes. A little later, the same phenomenon inside the room. Flies floundering across the room without direction, hitting the wall, falling to the ground.

The young, 'fit' people have decided on a 'breakout'. The three trucks in which the soldiers arrived are ready. They intend to head south, towards the French Mediterranean coast, travelling by night and hiding from the sun during the day. After sunset the trucks are loaded with all that had been made ready. They are also taking the weapons with them. Christine wanted to stay rather than desert us. But that is out of the question. Tina and I will deal with death alone. I hold out no hope for the twenty-eight young people, it is true, but the attempt is worthwhile. Dying is something one can do anywhere. Perhaps things are really a little better in Southern Europe, the consequences of the nuclear explosions not as total as they are here. Perhaps a few will make it. They are strong, and perhaps their constitutions will help them to overcome the doses of radiation that they have already taken in. Perhaps they are immune to the epidemics and sicknesses that are now raging all over the world. They know that they dare not suffer even the slightest injury. A lot of 'perhapses'.

27th August, evening

Every container that can be sealed is being filled with petrol and loaded onto the trucks. We syphon it out of the supermarket's

171

storage tank with hoses. It will last them for 3000 kilometres, enough to get them to the South of France.

Then my farewell to Christine. It is final. I shall never see my daughter again. God, who ever you may be, be with this tiny remnant of humanity!

Alone with Tina. I have said nothing to her about Christine's leaving, this desperate bid to escape. A breakout in the middle of the prison!

The bleeding under her skin has increased. She is in fever. I am making her cold compresses. Periods in a comatose state are interspersed with periods of clarity. She is very peaceful. When she is conscious, we chat. We know that nothing can separate us now. We are free. We shall decide our final step.

28th August, mid-day

In the end, Tina actually spent a very peaceful night. But she cannot stand any more. I have it now too. Taking tablets to stop the vomiting. The first blue-red marks on my arms and neck. Fever, I feel cold. But it's still all right. Quite normal really.

Tina wants to go outside. I promise that for the evening, when the sun has gone down. 'This evening will be the time, darling,' she says. I know.

Astonishing how long the batteries of the cassette recorder have kept on working. We listen to Chopin and Mozart, Bach. Music! Life! Now that the fear has fallen away from us, we can enjoy it again. When Tina comes to, she is very clear, very much alive, with an almost ecstatic intensity. We are able to remember who we are. These moments are now our life.

28th August, midnight

Tina is no longer alive. Shortly before sunset, I carried her out onto the terrace. How light she was. She wanted to look at the sun one more time. The glowing ball of light no longer hurt the eyes. It bathed the deadly brown flecks in the ruptured sky with red-gold light. The warm sunshine seemed to ease the suffering in her face. Her head lay on my shoulder, I held her tightly, she stroked my arm and wiped the tears from my fevered eyes. The sun set. The only sound was that of our breath.

Then, after a while, she reached for the glass of water, put it to her lips. I helped her to drink it. Her right hand was draped around my neck. After a few minutes, life began to ebb from her. Her hand slipped away from my hair.

I now feel very alien here. How is it that I am still alive? I am probably the only one for a long distance around here. Death is in me, I sense it, I am part of a dying whole.

All those whom I loved and who were close to me are with me. How many there are! Christine is absent, but Andreas is there, standing between my parents with his arms around their shoulders. I shall come tomorrow at this time. I only want to bury Tina.

29th August, mid-day

Acrid smoke woke me from a dreamless, heavy sleep. I thought the house was on fire. But it was not the house – the horizon was in flames. As far as the eye could see. Swirling, pale-grey smoke tingling with the brown-flecked sky. The dried-out woods are burning, the landscape is turning into a vast funeral pyre. Billions upon billions of tons of ashes are being swept up into the air. Europe is making its final transformation into desert, swift and inexorable. That which took millions of years to arise is returning to its origins, becoming dust and ash. I hear the crackling of the fires. The history of mankind is ending in roaring and a swirl of smoke.

There are flames on top of the plateau too, soon the fiery roller will come down the hill and pass over this place. A magnificent funeral for Tina and me.

Nature is cleansing itself. It is cauterising a malignant, incurable growth. These flames are the end – and a beginning. Nature will regenerate itself, start again from the beginning. She has enough time to spend millions of years restoring order where mankind in a few millennia, finally in a few decades,

173

wantonly created imbalance. The integrity and the inexorable logic of this global process is breathtaking. What has appeared to me, as one of the last witnesses, during these days as an inferno, a catastrophe, apocalypse, is in truth the correcting of a massive mistake on nature's part. The film of creation is flickering back towards the beginning of life. Now there is no more question of right and wrong, guilt and innocence. Nature knows no guilt and therefore no expiation. All it knows is functions, connections and systems. It insists on completeness.

Make yourselves Lords of the Earth – that was the wrong advice, it seems. It would have been possible for us to make ourselves a home on this planet. But our capacity for practical reason was too weak. The history of mankind is over, but life continues to exist. Will the next attempt succeed any better?

The sea of flame has surrounded me. The air is hot, the first houses on the edge of the village are on fire. I emptied the glass containing the powder in one gulp. I can feel peace flowing through me. My body is beginning to drop away, there is no more pain. Now I shall lie down next to Tina. At long last, peace.

THE END